COWS FOR THE SMALLHOLDER

LAND AND LIVESTOCK LIBRARY

COWS FOR THE SMALLHOLDER

Valerie Porter

PELHAM BOOKS

To Rosie,
a cow with character,
generosity and a sense of humour.

PELHAM BOOKS

Published by the Penguin Group
27 Wrights Lane, London W8 5TZ, England
Viking Penguin Inc., 40 West 23rd Street, New York,
New York 10010, USA
Penguin Books Australia Ltd, Ringwood, Victoria, Australia
Penguin Books Canada Ltd, 2801 John Street, Markham,
Ontario, Canada L3R 1B4
Penguin Books (NZ) Ltd. 182–190 Wairau Road,
Auckland 10, New Zealand

Penguin Books Ltd, Registered Offices: Harmondsworth,
Middlesex, England

First published 1988

Copyright © Valerie Porter, 1988

British Library Cataloguing in Publication Data

Porter, Val
    Cows for the smallholder.—(Land and livestock
library).
1. Cows
I. Title   II. Series
636.2'083   SF197

ISBN 0-7207-1776-0

Made and printed in Great Britain by
Butler & Tanner Ltd, Frome, Somerset
Typeset by Goodfellow & Egan, Cambridge

CONTENTS

ACKNOWLEDGEMENTS

ADAS, Chichester and Guildford
Dr S. H. U. Bowie, DSc, FRS, FEng, FIMM (photograph, Shetland cow)
Milk Marketing Board
National Dairy Council.
Particular thanks to Mr J. Arthur Todd, UDD (Nottm), NDD, NDDT, the
ADAS South East Region Milk Products and Processing Adviser.
   Unless otherwise acknowledged, the photographs have been provided by
the author.

CONVERSIONS – METRIC/IMPERIAL

1 litre = 1.76 pints (0.22 gallons)
1 litre milk = 1.03kg   1kg milk = 0.97 litres
1kg milk = 1.71 pints (0.21 gallons) = 2.20lbs
1 pint milk = 0.57 litres or 0.585kg
1 gallon milk = 4.55 litres or 4.68kg
1 gallon milk = 10.32lbs
1lb milk = 0.45kg

1cwt = 50.80kg

1 hectare = 2.47 acres   1 acre = 0.40ha
1mm = 0.04 inches   1 inch = 2.54cm
1 metre = 3.28ft = 1.09yd   1 yard = 0.91m

Degrees Centigrade = (degrees Fahrenheit – 32)×5/9

APPROXIMATIONS
1in : 25mm
1ft : 300mm   9 litres : 2 gallons
1m : 1.1yd   1kg   : 2 pounds
4ha : 10 acres   50kg   : 1 cwt

$10°C = 50°F$, $15°C = 59°F$, $20°C = 68°F$, $25°C = 77°F$, $30°C = 86°F$, $35°C = 95°F$.

I

CONSIDERING COWS

'These myriads of cows stretching under her eyes from the far east to the far
west outnumbered any she had ever seen at one glance before. The ripe hues
of the red and dun kine absorbed the evening sunlight, which the white-
coated animals returned to the eye in rays almost dazzling . . . She found
herself on a summit commanding the long-sought-for vale, the Valley of the
Great Dairies, the valley in which milk and butter grew to rankness.'

[*Tess of the d'Urbervilles*, Thomas Hardy]

Look around you. Somewhere out there, you will probably see grassland –
the dominant characteristic vegetation of this country. Covering about
14,000,000 hectares, it makes up more than half the total land area of the
United Kingdom. Much of it is uncultivated and often unenclosed rough
grazing, on heaths, moors, commons, downs, hills and uplands, and the
rest is given over to permanent pasture or temporary grass leys.

The most populous domesticated mammal in this country is a species
which does not and cannot eat grass, apart from chewing an occasional
contemplative stalk of the stuff. Fortunately for those 56,000,000 humans,
there are also about 45,000,000 domesticated ruminants on these islands
which do eat grass and which can convert it into something people *can*
consume, like meat and milk.

Of these ruminants, perhaps 13,000,000 are cattle and about a third of
the cattle are cows, the majority of them dairy cows. The average UK dairy
herd numbers more than sixty cows and in every part of the country the
averages have doubled in the last twenty years. Dairy farming is big
business.

However, this book is not for the average dairy farmer. It is for the
smaller farms – those of less than 20 hectares, the family farms which
account for about 5% of all cows in England and Wales and which between
them run about 136,000 cows, mostly in herds of no more than twenty or
thirty.

Nor is it just for the 'small farmer' but also for the smallholder who, with
anything from half a field upwards, is wondering what to do with all that
grazing and is considering what livestock, or combination of livestock and

other enterprises, might make best use of the land and give the best returns, whether financially or in terms of a different kind of fulfilment. What are the options? Do cows have a place in the scheme of things? Does cow-keeping on a small scale make any sense at all in the late twentieth century?

Well, about 40% of all the agricultural holdings in the United Kingdom are less than 20 hectares, and about a quarter of all holdings are less than 10 hectares. About 5% of all dairy herds boast less than ten cows; another 10% have ten to nineteen, with similar percentages for herds of twenty to twenty-nine and thirty to thirty-nine, which means that more than a third of the farmers who have any dairy cows at all keep them in herds of less than forty. You are not alone, but nor are you one of the crowd.

The cow is a generous creature and her produce is far more than milk. Quite apart from her gifts to the dairy, she can also give growth and vigour to several calves a year, manure for the field and garden, tranquillity to those who seek it or satisfying labour to those who do not. A cow's feet are firmly planted on the ground but the soft, dreamy look in her eyes as she ruminates on her cud shows that she is much more than a four-legged milk factory. There's a depth to cows, and perhaps it is this which appeals to would-be cow-keepers, however modest or ambitious. But the dream will only survive and succeed if it, too, stands four-square on down-to-earth practicalities. There is far more to cow-keeping than leaning on a field gate in contemplation, or sharing the warmth of the byre on a winter's evening. To turn idle dreams into reality, first take time to appreciate both the advantages and the drawbacks of that reality.

In Britain, cow's milk and dairy produce have long been staple foods and will probably remain so, in spite of the trend towards fat-free diets. Cow's milk is the basis of a highly organised and efficient marketing organisation and selling cow's milk is a great deal simpler than trying to find specialist outlets for sheep or goat dairy produce. All you have to do is register your herd, extract the milk from your cows hygienically, cool it quickly and then sit back and wait for the monthly milk cheque. The daily milk lorry takes your milk away and you have no further concern with its processing, storage or marketing.

Yet entrepreneurial and creative streaks can still be well and truly satisfied. You do have the option to process and retail your own produce if you enjoy the challenge of dairying and selling, and if you can bear the red tape.

Or you can use the milk as nature intended, for rearing calves. You can choose a simple, free-range suckler system, or a more closely managed system in which the cows are brought in to suckle housed calves and, with luck, to accept more than just their own offspring; or you can combine dairying with calf-rearing by milking your cows and dividing the produce between hand-reared calves and the demands of the house, farm dairy or milk tanker. Or you can simply enjoy the company of a housecow or two – preferably at least two for the sake of the cow, who is essentially a herd animal.

The economic art of cow-keeping is to ensure that outputs show financial profit over the inputs, while at the same time the more important art of husbandry seeks to ensure that the cow's life is a good and pleasant one, if only because a satisfied cow is a better producer.

All cows give a meat crop as well as milk. If breeding and management are sensibly planned the income from their calves can be quite reasonable (though it bears no comparison to the market value of milk) and even at the end of her time an old cow's carcase can bring in some return. And cows are an appreciating asset for most of their lives: their value tends to increase, unlike that of your tractor.

Then there is manure which, on the small-scale farm, is a bonus rather than a burden. On large dairy enterprises slurry handling, containment and disposal are problems, but with only a few animals the dung and urine are combined with bedding straw rather than scraped wantonly into liquid lagoons, and the manure can be used to very good effect to enrich the soil with nutrients *and* humus. Recycling is the basis of natural ecology and our forefathers would have been aghast at the present-day abuse of such precious resources.

Above all, however, the cow is a milk producer and all cow enterprises employ her in that role directly or indirectly, whether as a pet paddock housecow who raises her own calf and provides the family with fresh milk, cream and butter, or as one of a handful of cows who are milked or who suckle calves, or as part of either a dairy or beef herd run on commercial lines. Sometimes the cow, while still providing milk, also fulfils a very different role – a rare breed on display at a farm park, a placid creature tolerating the ham-fisted attempts of student milkers, a commune milch cow, a womb for highly bred implanted embryos, a decorative orchard grazer, a parkland asset, or a glossy, shampooed parader at the show-ground. The cow is an amenable animal for those who like cows.

That basic liking for the species is essential. Prospective cow-keepers would do well to become acquainted with other people's cows before they decide to acquire their own, either by helping a local farmer or smallholder, or perhaps by becoming a Milk Marketing Board (MMB) recorder and seeing cows at their worst in foot-freezing winter milking parlours at four o'clock in the morning. Even better, join your friendly local veterinary surgeon on his rounds and then you will not only find out whether you like cows but will also gain first-hand experience of their problems and how to

Cows for the Smallholder

deal with them. It will teach you a lot more than any part-time course at an agricultural college.

Every cow is very much an individual, which is why traditionally cows have endearing names like Daisy, Buttercup, Rosie, Fidget, Sod or Maybe (maybe she will, maybe she won't). Even in the huge dairy herds of the present day, when cows are numbered rather than named, individuals refuse to be anonymous. They ensure that the herdsman recognises their different temperaments and preferences, whether because they are always first into the parlour, or always spook at the third bay from the right, or consistently knock off their clusters, or wilfully flick a well-aimed dung-laden tail, or come along quietly and reliably, or give an irresistible flutter of long eyelashes. Even in the smallest herd there will be likeable cows, peaceful cows, cows admirable for their spirit and sense of adventure, and cows guaranteed to make everyone lose their temper. The smaller the herd, the more obvious the character, and the family whose housecow is a bad-tempered kicker should not judge the entire bovine race by her; they should let her suckle her calf or sell her. Instead they should seek a character who suits them better and gives the pleasure and contentment that so many cows do in return for a comfortable life with regular routines and a good measure of conversation and off-hand affection. Like any creature, human or otherwise, cows respond well to quiet kindness and it is said that the ideal cow handler is a self-confident introvert who is not in the least shy about talking affable nonsense to the animals and gives them plenty of friendly strokes and scratches.

If you like cows in general and think that cow-keeping might be feasible, think at least twice. First, check the practical aspects. It is difficult to generalise about the amount of land needed per cow because so much depends on local conditions, breed and size of cow, style and intensity of management, adequacy of husbandry, access to funds for bought-in food, whether and how calves are to be raised, what returns are expected or needed, available time and so on. In 1823, William Cobbett, that famous pamphleteer and champion of the rural labourer who travelled the country-side observing its iniquities, claimed that you could feed a cow on 40 rods (about a third of a hectare) but it was almost a full-time job to grow the crops on that land for the cow to eat.

For self-sufficient forage (i.e. seasonal grazing and home-grown con-served grass for the winter) you should allow perhaps half a hectare or an acre of reasonable pasture per Friesian or Shorthorn cow. You can run four Jerseys on the same acreage as three Friesians, and three Dexters to every two Friesians. Your first task is to decide how many animals the available land and resources can support in practice rather than in theory. Grass does not grow on trees: if you manage good lowland grass intensively, you increase the yield of the grass but that does not necessarily mean you can run more cows per unit area because the ground itself may not be able to take the pressure. Of course, buying in hay effectively buys extra land per cow, especially if your land poaches easily.

You must also think about housing. A suckler herd of hill-breed cows has minimal housing requirements but a high-yielding dairy cow on heavy land needs milking facilities and proper winter quarters with exercise areas, both for her own sake and to protect the next season's grazing, and also (though surely a secondary consideration) for the sake of her handlers.

For single sucklers allow perhaps half a hectare per cow (three times as much if it is rough grazing). Double or multiple sucklers might need a little more – say threequarters of a hectare per cow. For fattening strong store cattle, allow a third of a hectare in summer. For other beef enterprises, the area will, of course, vary according to the animals' ages and sizes.

Other considerations are less easily defined. You need to consider your neighbours. Can you ensure that your boundaries are stockproof in all circumstances, and will the endless bawling of a bulling cow or a deprived fresh-calver be tolerable?

What about your produce: can you find an outlet for it? Can a milk tanker make its way through the narrow lanes and right up to the milk-room? Can you find ways of making good use of the several thousand litres of milk your housecow will pour out every year? Are you suitably placed for other enterprises like tourist attractions and farm shops, and, if so, what are your chances of obtaining planning permission or raising the capital (or grants) for building conversions or new buildings? Are your fields accessible for tractors and trailers laden with hay or silage grass? Do you have the mechanical ability to manage your grazing or do you have access to a reliable, affordable contractor? (Making hay with a scythe and wooden rake is romantic, but . . .) Can you find relief milkers or calf-feeders when you need them? Are you on good terms with a local vet who likes and knows about cattle? What about insurance?

Think, and think again. Livestock of any kind entail commitment: they make demands on time, muscle power, finances and patience. A cow in milk is the biggest tie of all: her udder needs to be relieved of its burden twice a day, *every* day, for something like nine or ten consecutive months in every year, winter and summer, through your own sickness or health, and if you have more than one cow it is likely that you will be milking every single day of the year, including Christmas. The supply cannot be switched on and off at the mains. Even if the cows are suckling, they still need at least a twice-daily check to see that they are happy and there are no problems or unexpected disasters like arguments with the fencing or troubles with a ditch or sudden bloat from too much new grass and clover. Heifers and steers are expert at escaping into neighbouring gardens, especially on

Cows for the Smallholder

Sunday mornings. Calves need even more careful supervision: they can always find trouble without looking for it. Livestock need a human presence and if you are not able to commit yourself or a deputy whole-heartedly to their well-being, then you should not keep animals. By confining and exploiting them, you make them dependent upon you. That is quite an awesome responsibility, not to be too lightly undertaken.

GOING AHEAD

Whatever your enterprise, someone somewhere wants to know about it, register it or license it. When you first take over a holding (or start one from scratch), inform your local government agency and let them know what stock you have or propose to have. In England contact the Ministry of Agriculture, Fisheries & Food (MAFF); in Wales, talk to the Welsh Office Agricultural Department (WOAD). In Scotland the appropriate authority is the Department of Agriculture and Fisheries for Scotland (DAFS) and in Northern Ireland it is the Department of Agriculture for Northern Ireland (DANI). Incidentally, you will be unable to obtain grants if your holding is not registered.

In any event you will find it useful to talk to the local advisory officers about possibilities as well as realities. The MAFF, for example, provides its Agricultural Development and Advisory Services (ADAS) and as from 1st April, 1987, English farmers have had to pay for ADAS advice – which is a rude shock to those who have valued and relied upon the Ministry's free advice and leaflets for many years. In the long run it must be a fee worth paying and in any event you are obliged to register your holding and herd with the MAFF and to follow their rules, so it is best to look upon your ADAS adviser and the Ministry's Divisional Veterinary Officer (DVO) as friends from the start. By the nature of their work they are in contact with a lot of other local farmers and also have a nationwide database on which to formulate their advice, so the consumer (the farmer) should be able to benefit enormously from the breadth of their knowledge and in-depth understanding of local conditions, practices and markets. ADAS fees can seem disproportionately high for a smallholder but your adviser can give you up-to-date information about the many and varied grants which might be available and which could make all the difference to the financial success of your chosen enterprise. He can also tell you about the ever-changing EEC decisions and regulations which will affect your management methods and profits without so much as a by-your-leave.

The Government controls disease in the national herd and for that reason needs to know the movements of all livestock – where from, where to and when – and every owner of cattle must keep a Movements Record Book which is inspected at intervals. *All* movements must be recorded – not just permanent disposals but also temporary removals like going to a show or a bull being loaned to another farm. You might also be required to obtain a licence before moving an animal to or from your holding, especially if you are in an area affected by a reportable or notifiable disease.

Dairy farming can involve anything from one housecow to a whole herd, and can entail wholesale milk production and/or all kinds of processing and retailing of dairy produce. If you have cows which produce milk that you intend to sell rather than (or as well as) use in the house or to feed your calves and pigs, you must first obtain Government permission to do so (yes, even for one cow) by applying for registration as a dairy farmer to MAFF, WOAD, DANI or in Scotland to the local authorities. If your application is accepted, you become bound to comply with regulations concerning clean milk production and you must have a building in which to milk – a building which meets the requirements of the Milk & Dairies Regulations. Your premises, cows and methods will be inspected at regular intervals, with or without warning.

Next you must apply to your area MMB to register as a producer of milk and to sign a contract. You will also need a quota (see Chapter 10). The different regional boards have slightly different methods and nomen-clatures but in general they are responsible for regulating the marketing of milk. They are effectively farmers' co-operatives: farmers, as registered milk producers, give the boards the authority to operate as independent producers' organisations, within a legal framework. The broad rule is that all milk producers who offer milk for sale must sell it only to or through the boards, unless they are specially exempt. Your local board has a statutory obligation to buy your milk (even from a mere one or two cows, if registered) and to market it, provided it is of a certain standard of quality and cleanliness. There are several categories. You can be a Wholesale Producer selling all your milk to the board, which guarantees to buy every litre as long as it is of marketable quality. Or you can register as a Producer Retailer if you want to sell part or all of your own milk and its products on a retail basis direct to the final consumer rather than wholesale to the board; and in this context you can also apply for a special licence to sell your milk 'raw' rather than heat-treated. Or you can register as a Producer Processor if you want to process and sell liquid milk other than by retail to the final consumer. Or you can have a special contract as a Farmhouse Cheese-maker.

Although the MMB is bound to buy your milk if you are registered as a dairy farmer with the Ministry, those who have only a handful of cows may have problems because the board will insist on the milk being cooled to certain temperatures in a certain length of time and this could mean having to install a bulk tank. No one makes bulk tanks suitable for two cows!

Cows for the Smallholder

The great majority of milk producers register as wholesale producers because it is much the simplest option. If you decide to sell some of your milk on any other basis, you need a Ministry licence for untreated milk. Your local authority (normally the district or borough council) is responsible for the registration of distributors and dairies, and if you want to sell milk (whether untreated or processed) from your own premises you need a special licence and will be subject to all kinds of inspections by environmental health and trading standards officers, in the public interest. Do get to know these local officers: seek their advice in the early stages and try and see them as allies rather than enemies. They are not so much out to get you as to protect everyone else's health.

The situation for suckler cows is much simpler. If you undertake not to sell any milk or milk products from your holding you do not have to register with the MMB. You could well be entitled to join the EEC Suckler Cow Premium Scheme if you spend at least half your total working time in farming and derive at least half your total income from it. The premium is paid for the maintenance of any breed of suckler cow provided that she is in a herd used for rearing calves for meat production, and if she is a recognised dairy or dual-purpose breed she must be crossed to a bull of a recognised beef breed. Further, if you farm in a 'less favoured' area you might also receive EEC aid in the form of compensatory annual allowances for breeding your cattle (Hill Livestock Compensatory Allowances) but you must occupy at least 3 hectares of eligible land in hill areas in danger of depopulation in Scotland, Wales, Northern Ireland, northern England or southwest England. These areas also attract higher rates of grants under the Agricultural and Horticultural Development Scheme (AHDS) and the Agricultural and Horticultural Grant Scheme (AHGS).

You do not have to be a hill farmer to choose beef sucklers. Although very often such an enterprise is the best way of utilising upland grazing, it is also a good method of maximising the potential of inaccessible grazing areas on lowland holdings or of grazing a grass break-crop and using arable by-products.

Beef farming at its simplest can be single suckling on free-range hill land or can be increasingly intensive – double or multiple suckling, or artificial rearing and early weaning before raising calves on any of the various intensive or extensive beef systems that take calves to the finished stage, ready for market.

Other possibilities are discussed in Chapter 10, which gives you inspirations about rare breeds, education, opening to the public, showing, draught animals, smoked meats . . . the stuff of dreams for some.

The question of viability in terms of scale is a difficult one to answer and it is well worth talking to ADAS about it. They will probably tell you that the minimum dairy herd size from which any kind of reasonable living can be made by a full-time farmer is forty cows. In some parts of the country you can do it with half that number, especially with access to commonland.

At the other end of the scale, if you have perhaps a couple of housecows and are not trying to push their yields to commercial levels and do not take account of your own time or labour, then you will be at least self-sufficient and, if you are judicious in breeding and feeding, you might make a few hundred pounds on rearing the calves for beef, or rather more on making a very good cheese. Leon Downey (a former viola player with the Halle Orchestra) has turned a vague dream into a thriving business in ten years: he and his wife settled on a 7ha holding at Castle Morris, near Haverford-west, and bought themselves a housecow, knowing nothing at all about cows. They now have a herd of eighteen Jerseys and make nearly 8,000kg a year of their own Llangloffan Farmhouse Cheese in a beautifully converted old cowshed. The demand for their product greatly exceeds the supply, and they also find the whole cheese-making process is quite an attraction for their many visitors.

Your housecows or half a dozen milkers or sucklers will only give you profit (and even a living) if you can find an outlet for their produce and a good way of marketing it. You will not be able to support youself, let alone your family, with a few cows and nothing else but you will have the benefit of knowing exactly what has gone into the milk you drink and the meat you eat. You will also have the pleasure of the company of animals who can give you much more than material benefits.

The novice may not appreciate the fact that even a humble housecow can produce around twenty litres of milk a day in her peak yield period a few weeks after calving. Quite often the potential value of that milk is wasted, and the chapter on milk looks more closely at this aspect. Milk surplus often stimulates new enterprises – like pig-keeping – and once you have a cow you may well find your enterprise expanding almost unintentionally in quite unexpected directions. Unless you are interested in marketing, however, and are prepared to work at it, your handful of cows could very easily become a financial liability rather than an asset. Enough of inspiration, then: if you are still willing, let's get down to the daily realities of cow-keeping.

II

WHICH COW?

Cows today are specialists. They have been developed into numerous different breeds, each breed being originally evolved for a purpose and to meet specific local requirements.

Cattle breeds are generally described as either dairy or beef type. Some are dual-purpose, giving reasonable milk yields and also producing beefy calves, and some are triple-purpose, adding enough size for draughtwork to their milk and meat qualities. Some are even now in the course of changing their type from one purpose to another, chasing the elusive markets that will determine their future.

A dairy-type cow is generally wedge-shaped whether viewed from the side or from above. She is quite fine about the head and shoulders and much deeper and broader towards the back or 'business' end, where she

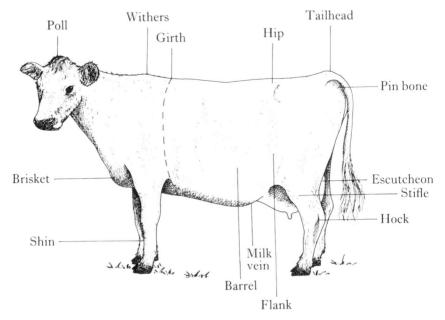

The points of a cow

produces her milk and carries and gives birth to her calf. A beef type is generally rather more square from all angles – stocky, solid and meaty with particular emphasis on the prime meat cuts at the rump and loin.

A good suckler cow is dual-purpose: she has something of both dairy and beef types. She is roomy enough to carry a good-sized calf and, like a dairy cow, is quite wide in the pelvis for easy calving. Her milk yields are rather less than those of a purebred dairy cow but generous enough to give fast growth to her calf. She is generally much hardier than a dairy cow, able to live on rougher grazing, less fussy about her food, willing to go on conceiving and rearing her annual calves for anything up to twenty years, and maintaining a strong, protective mothering instinct which could be a disadvantage in a dairy cow, whose calf is normally removed from her at a very early age. The suckler is stockier than the dairy cow and she can pass on useful beef-making genes to her calf – unless she is simply a vehicle for carrying a transplanted embryo, which is a role likely to be more extensively developed in the future.

BEEF

Genuine beef breeds vary in their rate of growth and in their eventual mature weight. A growing animal develops its bone structure first, then the lean muscle, and finally it puts on fat of different kinds. Late-maturing breeds characteristically have a high growth rate but defer laying down fat until they reach a greater weight and greater age than early-maturing cattle on a similar diet. Early-maturing breeds fed intensively on cereals would start putting on fat before they reached a marketable weight and are therefore much better suited to extensive (grazing) systems, when they can be slaughtered younger so that the meat is tender. Slow-growing breeds seem to produce tastier meat, ripening like a good cheese, but they can take two or three years to reach the slaughterhouse, in which time they have eaten quite a lot (though of less expensive feedstuffs), taking up space on the holding and tying up capital. But perhaps a West Highland raised for five years on peat and heather, as they say, is financially as good a bet as a big Continental cross raised for a year or two on expensive protein concentrates, crammed into the beast as if it was a goose destined for pâté de foie gras. What counts ultimately is food conversion rates: the ability to convert food into meat cheaply, and to put that meat in the right tissues (lean rather than fat) in the right places.

It may seem out of place to discuss beef in a book about cows but in fact the beef industry toes the line to the dairy industry in this country and the two are inextricably linked. Most beef comes from pure or crossbred dairy calves and cull dairy cows; the rest is from suckled calves of dual-purpose or beef cows, cull beef cows and imported Irish stores.

In the second half of the 1980s, however, dairy farmers are confronted by EEC milk lakes and quotas. Quotas are only applicable to milk destined to be sold for human consumption in one form or another, and it is therefore worth any cow farmer's while, be the herd large or small, to think about channelling the cows' milk into other outlets such as beef. Thus beef very definitely has a place in a book about cows, especially when the EEC is forecasting a reduction of 900,000 UK dairy cows by the year 2000. Perhaps, once again, this country will swing back to the dual-purpose breeds which served our ancestors so well for centuries.

CHOOSING THE RIGHT COWS

It is for you to decide not only whether milk is more important than beef, or whatever other enterprise you envisage, but also which breed or combination of breeds is best suited to the aims of your enterprise.

You should certainly consider the area in which you farm when selecting a breed. Go for the local type if you can: it was *designed* for your part of the country and, as many of the regional breeds are low in numbers, there is something worthwhile in identifying with your local one and giving it a home in its native countryside. Or see what other local farmers stock: they will have sound commercial reasons for their choice of breed.

However, your choice will probably be influenced by your heart as much as your head. The breed descriptions which follow give general practical guidance but whereas some people may fall for the eyelashes of the Jersey, others cannot resist the appealingly ridiculous face of a Belted Galloway, the striking colour pattern of a British White, or the fine horns of a Longhorn, whereas the more down-to-earth may look no further than Friesians or Holsteins. Bear in mind that averages are only averages and the yields of individual cows or herds may be considerably lower or higher than those given here; likewise milk quality may vary, though not to such extremes as yield. Milk yields and average cow sizes will also depend on where and how the cows are farmed. Remember, too, that a breed described as naturally horned can (and often does) have its horns removed when it is a very young calf. If you need to know more about a breed, contact its breed society but take societies' glowing appraisals with a little pinch of salt: they exist to promote the breed and may forget to draw your attention to its less attractive qualities.

Your choice will also be affected by availability. Any local market or farm can offer the standard breeds; others may be easily obtainable in their own parts of the country but not elsewhere, and the rare breeds are altogether more difficult to locate. Try the Rare Breeds Survival Trust (RBST) annual show and sale in September at Stoneleigh, or become a member of the Trust and keep an eye on the classified advertisements in its monthly magazine, *The Ark*. It is also worth checking publications aimed at smallholders, who on the whole are more likely than large farms to go for rare breeds.

Buy animals direct from a farm whenever you can: markets are bound to be traumatic for them and anyway it is useful to see your potential purchase in its own environment, where you can assess temperament more easily. Temperament is important because cow-keeping should be a pleasure rather than a continual confrontation. In a dairy cow you want an animal that comes happily into the parlour and likes her food; and you can tell a lot about the cow (and about the stockman) by watching her in the parlour during normal milking routines. If you are buying direct from a recorded dairy herd you will be able to check each cow's MMB records for yield, milk quality, regularity of calving and so on.

If you are a novice wanting a housecow, start with an older cow being sold off by a commercial farmer because her yields or udder are no longer up to his high standards. She will make a very adequate housecow, giving plenty of milk for your needs and being wise in the ways of calving. A heifer might be cheaper but she is an unknown quantity and will probably not be used to handling. The ideal is a cow who is in calf for the second or third time and is about three or four years old: she still has a good, long productive life ahead of her and a past record for reference.

Whatever the breed, and whatever the source, look for a healthy animal with bright eyes, a general air of alertness, sound feet and joints, adequate teeth (especially the grinding molars) and a thin, pliable skin with a good bloom to it. Check that the herd is brucellosis accredited and tuberculosis free. Check the udder – that vital accessory! If you are machine milking, avoid a low-slung udder which hampers the attachment of the clusters, and if you are hand-milking try and get four teats that are big enough to get hold of. In a Jersey, for example, you may find that the back teats are quite small (finger-and-thumb jobs) and as most of the milk comes from the back quarters you are likely to find milking hard work.

If you have a chance, stand in the field with the cows. If the ones you have your eye on approach you with mild curiosity, so much the better. If you are buying sucklers, however, they are naturally more timid than dairy cows, which are used to human contact in the parlour, and so they should be: the suckler must have an instinct to protect her calf.

Now for the breeds. They are listed in alphabetical order rather than by category because quite often it is up to you what role they will actually fulfil.

ABERDEEN ANGUS
[*Beef. Black. Polled.*]
The prime pure beef breed – short, stocky, and famous worldwide for

quality meat. Early maturing, low mature bodyweight, slow growth rate. Fine bones, even fat deposition.

AYRSHIRE

[Dairy. Reddish brown and white. Horned.]
Pretty cow with classic wedge shape of true dairy animal. Average mature cow 127–135cm at shoulder, 490–590kg. Best udder of all breeds – all of apiece rather than four disparate quarters, and much less likely to sag or become misshapen. Pleasant temperament and as economical as any other Scot. Good milk for cheese. Purebred calves not good for beef but crosses well with Friesian, Hereford, red breeds or Continental bulls for suckled beef calves. Average milk yield about 5,000kg, average butterfat 3.9%.

AYRSHIRE Hitcham Marie, champion dairy cow at 1987 Royal Bath & West Show.
[Farmers Weekly]

BRITISH WHITE

[Dual-purpose. White with black or red muzzle, ears, teats, fetlocks and freckles. Polled (some scurred).]
Rare breed originally found in Lancashire and East Anglia. Now becoming more commercial and its numbers are growing. Breeders tending to emphasise beef qualities rather than milk. Useful single suckler. Good

BRITISH WHITE bull and calf

results from crosses to Continental bulls; also British White bulls on Friesian or Galloway cows, but not on heifers of smaller breeds (some calves very deep in brisket and could cause calving problems).

CONTINENTAL BREEDS
Continental bulls are often used on dairy-breed cows to put a bit of beef on their calves. The Continentals are large and well muscled, partly because they continued to be used as draught animals long after British breeds had become beef specialists. Be careful with choice of breed and selection of sire. For example, Jersey cows with their wide pelvises usually calve quite easily with all but the heftiest calves, but, surprisingly, a big Friesian cow can have problems. The most popular Continentals, all of them horned, are probably the Charolais (white or creamy), Limousin (dark yellowish-brown), Simmental (red and white), Blonde d'Aquitaine (straw coloured), Maine Anjou (red and white) and Chianina (white with black points). The Belgian Blue (blue and white) is currently fashionable, with extreme double-muscling at the back end – so much so that Belgian Blue cows quite often have to be calved by means of a Caesarean.

DEVON
[*Beef. Red. Polled or horned.*]
High growth rate but great variety within breed. Originally triple-purpose with rich milk, ability to finish rapidly for beef, heavy build for draught-

work. Emphasis now on beef – good suckler cow (average mature weight 590kg). Bull useful on Friesian, Highland, Ayrshire, Shorthorn etc. Ideally suited for native Exmoor with thick, curly, mossy, waterproof coat. Milk yield can reach 4,500kg with proper management; good butterfat.

DEXTER
[Dual-purpose. Black, red or dun. Horned.]
The favourite smallholders' cow – a small, solid, short-legged Irish mountain breed of character. Go for longer legged type (up to 112cm at shoulder, preferably about 100cm) rather than lines bred too much for dwarfish size as ornamental curiosities (from 90cm) which could produce breeding problems and throw 'bulldog' calves. Hardy enough for any-where; adaptable to good pasture as well as poor hill grazing. Used commercially both in recorded dairy herds (perhaps 2,000–3,000kg at more than 4% butterfat) and as beef sucklers (small quality joints ideal for the freezer). Slow growing, never gets very heavy and cannot be forced. Small size means high stocking rates and comparatively small appetite. Avoid steaming up before calving. Used to be rare breed but numbers have risen fast.

DEXTER Knotting Little Ladyrush. [Jane Paynter]

BRITISH FRIESIAN
[*Dairy. Black and white, some red and white. Horned.*]
The most common breed in the UK: accounts for most of our milk and more than 70% of home-grown beef (pure Friesian, or crossed to beef-breed bull). British breed now distinct from original Dutch type – bigger (average mature cow about 600kg, 140cm at shoulder) and emphasis on dairy but almost classifiable as dual-purpose – has taken over that role from older native breeds like Shorthorn. Late-maturing beef, high growth potential, good for intensive beef as pure or crossbred and finishes well. Average milk yield about 5,700kg, 3.8% butterfat. Small farmer or specialist may prefer something less obvious and less hungry or may want better milk quality.

BRITISH FRIESIAN. [Nigel Stone]

GALLOWAY
[*Dual-purpose. Black or dun, whole or with white belt, or white with black points. Polled.*]
Standard Galloways are very common on rough upland and moorland grazing but the 'Beltie' was classified as a rare breed until 1986. Stocky,

ABOVE: *BELTED GALLOWAY family group.* [R.B.S.T.]
BELOW: *GLOUCESTER*

medium-sized animal; average mature cow weighs about 475kg. Woolly double coat for waterproofing and insulation; exceptionally hardy and long-lived, able to convert rough grazing into good lean beef. Low growth rate, early maturing. Excellent sucklers. Belties have more milk than standard Galloway and have been milked in dairy herds. Cows cross well to Whitebred Shorthorn (for a Blue–Grey) or Continental bulls. White Galloways have similar qualities to standard black or dun but are white with black ears, eyelids, muzzles and feet.

GLOUCESTER
[*Dairy. Mahogany with white finch-back. Horned.*]
Originally a triple-purpose breed (milk, meat and draught), now more emphasis on milk, especially for cheese-making (small fat globules, good butterfat and protein levels). If properly bred for better milk, could yet be reinstated as a dairy cow but too few animals currently recorded to give sensible yield/quality figures. Numbers very low indeed and RBST status 'critical'.

ENGLISH GUERNSEY
[*Dairy. Golden tan and white. Horned.*]
Golden cow with amber hooves, sandy eyelashes and high quality 'gold top' milk with large fat globules – good for butter-making. Cream sets very

GUERNSEY. [M.M.B.]

readily. Pigmented skin gives yellowish fat in carcase; not good for purebred beef but can cross usefully with Angus, Hereford or Continental beef bulls. Quite small, light cow (about 430kg) so stocking rates can be high. Average milk yield 4,000kg, butterfat 4.63%.

HEREFORD
[Beef. Red and white, white face. Horned.]
The standard British beef bull – colourmarks all its calves with instantly recognisable white face. Early maturing, fairly high growth rate. Heavy weight at finish; heavy boned; good performance on grass. Bull crosses well with most breeds but now rapidly losing ground to Continental bulls.

HIGHLAND
[Beef. Cream or fawn to very dark brown. Horned.]
Shaggy coat, heavy fringe, characteristic sweeping 'handlebar' horns. Small, short-legged breed from Scottish Highlands and Western Isles, popular in own area. Can outwinter in worst possible weather and prefers not to be confined. Hardiest of all cows, useful for moorland and poor hill grazing; most efficient at converting low-cost feed into quality beef. Even better if crossed to Shorthorn. Very slow growing and late maturing but breeders now concentrating on improving this. Average mature cow weight about 545kg. Mothers aggressively protective of new calves.

HIGHLAND

BRITISH HOLSTEIN
[*Dairy. Black and white. Horned.*]
Originally from same stock as the Friesian and increasingly popular in Britain. Developed largely in North America for milk quantity, with less emphasis on beef than in the Friesian. Very big animal (mature cow about 145cm at shoulder, average 680kg), rather bony, giving huge milk yields but little flesh for beef. Recent popularity in UK probably due to quotas: claimed that higher yields from fewer animals may be more efficient in terms of energy for milk production. Not so much an increase in purebred cows, more a case of pumping Holstein genes into Friesians to boost milk yield. Average yield 6,250kg, butterfat 3.75%.

IRISH MOILED
[*Dairy. Red and white with white finching. Polled.*]
The rarest breed of all, now down to double figures, all recently moved to England under protective eye of RBST. Serious inbreeding problems. Dual-purpose but with emphasis on milk yield and ability to do well on poor land. Economical, easy calving, docile. Numbers far too low for recorded milk yields, but yields high for minimal input. Small to medium-sized cow.

IRISH MOILED calf

JERSEY

[*Dairy. Wide colour range – very light fawn or grey to tan and rich chestnut to darker smoky colour, sometimes broken-coloured with white; black muzzle with mealy ring. Horned.*]

Pretty cow with languid eyes. Small and decoratively dainty (mature cow about 120cm, 385kg) but easy calver (wide pelvis). Purebred calves no good for butcher but Continental crosses for intensive beef or to Angus or Hereford for extensive. Famous for high-quality milk, the creamiest of all. Character cow, docile from generations of tethered grazing in Channel Islands, though some strains may be a little neurotic. Can be very affectionate: ideal housecow. Lower yield than Guernsey (average 3,900kg) but higher butterfat (5.18%) and can be tightly stocked. Good broad muzzle for efficient grazing.

JERSEY

KERRY

KERRY

[Dairy. Black. Horned.]

Attractive little Irish cow, graceful and agile. Productive for her size (average 122cm, 350–450kg) – average milk yield 3,300kg, 4% butterfat. Long productive life – will probably still be milking at twenty. Slow-maturing beef calf, excellent flavour. High stocking rate. Increases in size and yield on good pasture but can do well enough on much less – originally bred for exposed districts with scanty food supplies. Milk good for cheese and butter. Used to have close links with Dexter. Now a rare breed.

LINCOLN RED

[Beef. Cherry red. Polled.]

Big, hardy animal from Lincolnshire. Originally a Shorthorn; became polled mid-1950s. Used to be dual-purpose but now beef – finishes on grass in all sorts of climates. Rapid liveweight gain. Good suckler cow, or as bull on dairy and beef cows.

LONGHORN

[Dual-purpose. Light red roan to dark brindle, with white finching. Horns.]

Large, lean, handsome breed with eye-catching 'handlebar' horns. White

ABOVE: *LONGHORN cow and calves*

LEFT: *SHETLAND Wykham Fritillary.* [Stanley Bowie]

finching catches sunlight like a halo. Originally triple-purpose Midlands breed and once dominant throughout England. Now rare but making a comeback for beef. Long, lean carcase on rough grazing; can produce average 400-day weight of more than 475kg with 3.5mm backfat. Cow excellent suckler with lots of room for big calf and plenty of milk to rear it. Affable breed, much loved by those who farm it. Good results being achieved from Longhorn × Welsh Black suckler cows put to Charolais bull.

RED POLL
[Dual-purpose. Deep red. Polled.]
Good conversion rates for both milk and meat. Origins in famous milking Suffolk dun and beefy Norfolk Red. Chunky breed, average mature cow weight 520kg. Used today in recorded dairy herds (average yield 4,000kg at 3.9% butterfat) with long and even lactation; milk useful for cheese. Udder can become awkwardly pendulous. Also used as suckler. Early maturing, fairly rapid growth to fifteen months. No longer classified as rare breed in UK.

SHETLAND
[Dual-purpose. Black and white. Horned.]
A small crofters' cow, traditionally tethered by rope looped over horns. Used to come in a range of colours but now standardised to Friesian-like black and white. Can survive in toughest conditions on poorest of grazing, but will be much more productive with better treatment. Rare breed – critically so in 1979 at double figures but rescued by co-operation between DAFS and RBST. Impressive beef potential but beware of overfeeding either beef animals or breeding cows. Milk yields gradually improving. Have been some problems with artificial insemination (AI). Reputation for being one-person cows; make good housecows or sucklers.

SHORTHORN
[Beef and dairy types. Red, red and white, white, roan. Horned.]
Very much the dominant breed throughout nineteenth century and first half of twentieth, but numbers of pure Shorthorns in UK now dropping fast because of Friesian success. Offers something to everybody (well-marbled quality meat, hardiness, longevity, placid nature, adaptability) but Friesians have higher yields, slightly better butterfat percentages and faster growth rate. Major types in this country are Beef Shorthorn (centred in Scotland – recently classified as rare breed), Northern Dairy Shorthorn (also rare), and dual-purpose Dairy Shorthorn with its well-known variant the Whitebred Shorthorn of the Borders, which is used on Galloways to boost milk and produce the popular Blue–Grey suckler cow of Scotland. Beef type early maturing, similar size and growth rate to Angus but heavier

boned and less evenly fatted. Dairy Shorthorn acceptable beef but finishes less quickly than Beef type or Angus. Average mature Shorthorn cows perhaps 570kg; average milk yields about 5,000kg in Dairy types at 3.6% butterfat; perhaps better for cheese than for butter.

SOUTH DEVON
[*Dual-purpose. Yellowish brown to red. Horned.*]
Largest British breed, now a minority one even in own South Hams region. Average mature cow about 660kg. Few dairy herds left (average yield 3,300kg, 4.2% butterfat) but emphasis today mostly on beef. Late maturing, grows very fast on grass to give high liveweight before finishing; lean carcase.

SUSSEX
[*Beef. Rich dark red. Horned or polled.*]
Once triple-purpose – still working regularly as draught oxen until a few years ago. Now a prime beef animal, bulls being used particularly on Friesians for carcase with high ratio of muscle to bone and minimal offal waste. Later maturing than Angus; even fat, fine boned, better pure than crossbred. Average mature cow 560–610kg. Very similar to South Devon in type; grows fairly quickly. Excellent on grass: grazes without discrimination, leaving pasture even; often used to tidy up rough grazing.

WELSH BLACK
[*Dual-purpose. Black, and colour variations. Horned or polled.*]
Originally two types – a smaller, more compact beefy strain from North Wales and a larger, milkier Castlemartin type with longer legs in south. Dual-purpose hill breed but primarily beef now, though there are one or two pure dairy herds. Typical milk yield 3,000–4,000kg at 4% butterfat. Good suckler cow – does very well on very little and can take any kind of weather, protected by shaggy coat. Very easy calver with wide pelvis; excellent mother. Average mature cow 545kg, or considerably less in northern type. Long, even lactation – not much difference in yield over period. Long breeding life. Hardy, slow to mature but quite rapid for hill breed. Numerous colour variations but only black can be registered with Welsh Black Cattle Society. Others include bright red, blue, smokey, finch-backed, red belted, black belted, and white with black points.

OPPOSITE ABOVE: *SHORTHORN Villabrook Merry Maid 2nd, worth 1,000 guineas in 1986.* [Farmers Weekly]

BELOW: *BELTED WELSH*

WHITE PARK

[*Beef. White with black or red ears, muzzle, eyelids, teats, feet. Horned.*]
Striking breed with romantic history, and at present very rare but in good
hands. Specialist's breed needing careful, knowledgeable breeding (controlled by breed society) because of such low numbers. Potentially excellent
beef animal of great size (mature cow 560–660kg); good growth rates, good
conformation (average 3mm back fat). Also pure dairy herds (up to 4,500kg
at 4% butterfat). Cows make useful sucklers. Feral herd at Chillingham.

WHITE PARK cow and calf

III

UNDERSTANDING COWS

BEHAVIOUR PATTERNS

Whatever the breed, and whatever the individual character, a cow is a cow and her behaviour will echo, however faintly, the behaviour of her wild ancestors and cousins. An understanding of that behaviour is the key to cow management. Try and 'think cow': try to see, hear, smell, touch and taste things from the cow's point of view and experiences.

A wild cattle herd is generally based on quite a small group of cows and their offspring – perhaps a score or so – who form a fairly well-defined society in which each individual recognises all other individuals and forms hierarchical relationships with them. Bull calves in the group begin to dominate the females (including their own dams) from the age of about eighteen months and they leave the group soon after to join a bachelor herd, where from about two years old they gradually fight their way up the male social ladder. By four years old a bull has become decidedly territorial and grazes well apart from his male colleagues, frequently making threatening displays or posing on a convenient prominence which enables him to boast his size and strength without actually risking direct contact with an opponent. Serious fighting is only necessary when the position of an acknowledged 'king' bull is challenged. Normally threats are signal enough to cause withdrawal from a rival's territory, or at worst two males will blow off steam by bashing heads at 'fighting holes' scraped in the ground with horns and hooves. In such scraps the lesser bull usually retires early with little or no damage to either party. There seems to be a definable 'personal space' of about six metres around any bull: if another bull (or a human) encroaches on that space, the adrenalin rises and triggers threatening behaviour, but it drops again when the intruder withdraws beyond that crucial imaginary boundary. Every living creature has such a boundary, including humans, though the distance varies according to species and social context.

Cows also establish patterns of dominance among themselves, largely without actual fighting but showing who's who by means of butting – more like 'bunt and hook' orders than 'pecking' orders (bunt for polled, hook for horned). Seniority in age is a decided advantage between cows, and so is size or weight. Adult cows in a natural group will know their places and maintain the status quo for long periods. In a small herd, the hierarchy tends to be linear: A dominates, B, who dominates C, who dominates D and so on.

The situation is much more complicated in the unnatural herds regulated by domestication. A dairy herd, for example, is often many times larger than it would be in the wild and its composition is changed frequently as dry cows temporarily leave the milking herd or newly calved heifers join it. In beef systems any good stockman recognises that it is best to rear a batch from calfhood *within a stable group*, so that the same animals remain together right through to slaughter without being split up or having new animals introduced into the social structure which they have long since defined between themselves. Dairy heifer calves noticeably sort out a social order very early on and will maintain it right through to when they join the main milking herd.

Forced changes in the grouping can be quite traumatic for a species which would naturally remain in the same small herd for long periods. The changes inflict constant social pressure to re-establish a place in the scheme of things. Sometimes the structure of the domestic herd will still be basically linear, with newcomers establishing their rank by means of weight, strength or breed characteristics (in a mixed herd, for example, an Ayrshire tends to dominate a Jersey, or in a beef herd an Angus dominates a Shorthorn, which in turn dominates a Hereford, and a Highland gives way to just about any other breed in spite of its armoury of horns) but at the top of the hierarchy there may be an eternal triangle in which one animal dominates all the rest *except for one*, which in turn dominates all the herd except for a third, and that third animal is in turn dominated by the first (A dominates all except B, B dominates all except C, including A, and C dominates all except A). The triangle might also occur elsewhere in the hierarchy or might be more complex in that A, B and C are small groups within the herd rather than individuals – a sort of bovine gang warfare. Such a system of groups within a herd is a sensible way to compromise with the unnaturally large size of the farm herd, and in the interests of the cows it is a wise farmer who recognises group structures and aims to keep each group together by calving them at the same time of year.

Dominance does not necessarily equate with leadership. A 'leader' is one of a pool of cows who make the first move, perhaps to find a new stretch of grazing or to head for a drink. Cattle exhibit what behaviourists call allelomimetic behaviour, i.e. they tend to follow a leader's example and act generally in unison (at a leisurely pace) and the essence of herd life is co-ordinated activity. If a leader begins to settle down and ruminate, the rest of the group soon follows suit. Typically a leader is a middle-ranking cow and if the group is on the move the most dominant cows are quite often content to amble along in the middle of the group, not pushing to the front, though the lowest ranks will inevitably be trudging along at the rear. If the movement is a forced one – for example to the parlour at milking time – the line-up seems to be generally consistent on each occasion but not necessarily in the same order as if following a leader's voluntary direction.

However good the pasture, incidentally, cattle remember their nomadic ancestry and do like an occasional ramble for its own sake. Given the opportunity, a leader will take them off in Indian file for some exploratory ranging. That single-file formation accounts for the narrow tracks that quickly form in a field of grazing cattle.

In general cows are creatures of habit. Very broadly, a herd whose rhythm is not dictated by the demands of the parlour tends to have several major grazing periods in any twenty-four hours: at daybreak, mid-morning, mid-afternoon and at dusk, and also a shorter period around midnight. The total number of active grazing hours obviously depends on pasture quality, weather, general health and so on but usually adds up to perhaps eight or ten hours a day. Dairy cows tend to graze quite urgently after milking and also extend their midnight grazing to make up for time lost in the yard and parlour, but bulling cows are so busy mounting or being mounted that they spend much less of their time grazing and their milk yield can drop noticeably as a result.

Weather naturally affects herd behaviour. European cattle are a cold-weather species, with hairy coats and with central heating provided by the fermentation processes in the rumen. Hot weather causes them more stress than cold and they actively seek shade, or wallow, or at least paddle. Hot weather also reduces the desire for food which of course leads to a decline in productivity, but some breeds are much more adaptable to heat than others, especially those with pigmented skin.

Whatever the weather, rest is important whether they are loafing or actually lying down. About threequarters of the total rumination time is normally spent lying down, though there is a greater tendency to stand during wet weather. Rest of one kind or another may take up nine to twelve hours in twenty-four. There is often individual preference for which side to lie on and the normal position is with forelegs tucked under the body, one hind leg tucked forward beneath the bulk of the body to support it and the other out to the side. Some cows lie completely on their sides like a sleeping dog, but not for long periods.

Actual sleep is probably not much more than three or four hours in a day. The sleeping cow adopts a calf-like position with her head turned towards her flank. Individual sleeping patterns are regular except when calving is imminent, when the total sleeping time is often halved in the twenty-four hours before parturition. New quarters, especially stalls, can disrupt sleeping patterns for quite some time and the unsettled cow, too discomfited to sleep well, will be less productive. Other factors can affect her ability to relax enough to sleep properly, such as the traumatic removal of her calf or the social stress of entering a new group.

The size of a dairy herd may be unnaturally large, with all the added social stress which that entails (and which can be a source of all sorts of physical illnesses) but cattle can probably readily recognise up to about sixty or seventy individuals. (They have good memories too: a cow will recognise a once familiar human instantly, even after an absence of several years.) The sense of smell plays a part in identification but there is also visual recognition. Eyesight and hearing are not as keen as the sense of smell but are still good; for example, they can hear sounds beyond human range at both lower and higher frequencies. Like all prey animals, cattle have good panoramic vision: while they are grazing they have a wide peripheral visual range in which to glimpse a potential predator. A housecow can recognise her owner in the distance largely by stance or way of moving; that is, the cow has a general impression of the person rather than seeing them in detail at long range, and she probably catches their smell too. Cattle are partially colourblind and, of all colours, red is the one they are unlikely to distinguish. Tell that to the matador!

The sense of smell is acute in all cattle. It is used to catch the first whiff of approaching danger; it is employed ceaselessly in selecting palatable grazing; and it plays a major part in communication within the highly social context of the herd.

Sight, sound and smell combine when a cow is ready to mate. Cattle are not seasonal breeders and in the wild herd the separated bulls keep within range of the female groups all year round, using various senses to recognise a cow on heat. A bulling cow is generally restless and more vocal: her bellowing changes key and broadcasts a message as the appropriate time approaches but at distances on open range the bulls will probably be alerted by sight sooner than sound or smell. The activities of distant females mounting each other is a sure sign that one cow or another is in oestrus. Cow-on-cow mounting is a regular feature of domestic herds as well as wild ones.

In wild and feral herds the imminent calver tends to withdraw before parturition. She will be much less willing to rebuff lower-ranking cows and soon finds a private place away from the herd where she can give birth in peace. Like fawns, the newborn calves naturally 'lie up' for the first few days. After suckling, the mother returns to the herd and the calf remains hidden until she comes back again for the next suckling. Eventually the calf follows its mother back to the herd.

Once calves have been allowed to join the herd (and all the other cows, especially heifers, will take considerable interest in the newcomer – and will protect it from predators) a daily rhythm is soon established. Cows with calves tend to lie together in groups. At dawn, the cows rise and the calves suckle then move away from the cows to lie down in a 'crèche' while the cows graze. Within a few hours one or two calves begin to call; their mothers return to suckle and, cows being cows, very soon the whole group is having a mass suckling session. The pattern continues with another session in the afternoon and a suckling and grooming session in the evening (grooming is an important part of social life in any herd) and the group comes together again at dusk to see the night through in company. Thus the calves have already learned to be part of a herd and to co-ordinate their activities. Gradually they sort out their own social hierarchy within that herd.

HANDLING

In handling cattle, exploit their natural behaviour rather than fight it. Bear it in mind when you are designing accommodation and management techniques, and, above all, bear in mind that a contented cow in a stable social group will be much more productive than one which is unsettled and unhappy because her basic psychological and physical needs have been misunderstood or ignored. Always treat cows kindly, quietly, confidently and with patience, and maintain social contact with them by continual friendly conversation and reassuringly firm physical contact. A fluttering or suddenly thrust-out hand or a tentative, dabbing caress will alarm rather than relax a cow.

In the domestic herd some of the natural behaviour patterns are masked by management systems but the aim should still be to reduce stress, distress and boredom by making due allowances for natural lifestyles. Perhaps the major points to bear in mind are that cattle are *social* animals: they need and seek close contact with each other, and isolation (or the threat of it) is traumatic. Also understand the concept of space, which is important to cattle. First there is a home range – a habitual territory for the whole group and somewhere to which individuals tend to return, given the chance. Variety within that space is important – a flat, empty, featureless plain is much less accommodating than an area with rises and hollows and clumps of trees or shrubbery which can screen an animal from view as well as give it shelter.

Then there is personal space, which has several facets. Personal space includes the area an animal needs physically, giving it enough room to stand, lie down, stretch etc., and within this space the area around the head is crucial because the head is probably the most constantly active part of the animal, used for eating, sniffing, grooming, gesticulating and establishing relationships with others. There is also social space, a distance habitually maintained between the animal and its fellows, and a flight space which is the distance comfortably maintained between the animal and a potential threat or a stranger and which, in the cow's relationship with humans, is gradually reduced by regular handling and familiarisation.

All these personal spaces play a part in social relationships, and the head space seems to be the most jealously guarded of all. With cattle, that space is about a metre in radius and of course a good sweep of horns helps to keep it secure. A sudden or unexpected intrusion into a cow's flight space, and particularly into her head space, may cause a defensive reaction that will surprise you.

The thoughtful cow-keeper will ensure that stock are befriended from a very early age and are used to being handled for welcome reasons like feeding (never underestimate the value of cupboard love). But inevitably sucklers out on the hill are much less used to people than are dairy cattle and their reaction to an approach is bound to be more suspicious. In an ideal situation, always let cows come to you rather than march up to them and infringe on their flight space. Stand quietly with your arms hanging down or your hands pocketed and let the animals' curiosity get the better of them. If you are wearing an aged jacket they will soon be licking it or chewing it (and your footwear), showing an almost cannibalistic preference for suede and leather. Any cow, incidentally, however used to handling, will spook at flapping clothes and particularly at white overalls which are inevitably associated with undignified encounters with vets, MAFF inspectors or artificial insemination (AI) technicians.

Cattle have long memories and a cow will remember a bad experience for several years, readily associating a particular location or person with that experience. Electric fencing is a typical illustration of this in the short term: if a cow has been trained to respect an electrified wire, she might not cross the boundary it defined for quite a while after the wire has been removed, and she will also respect a perfectly innocent strand of baler twine, for a time. She can also be fooled by a false cattle-grid of lines painted on the ground.

Early experiences with humans, buildings and equipment need to be good ones; be prepared to give a fair amount of time to early training and familiarisation sessions because it will save you so much more time in the long run. A cow might be with you for as many as twenty productive years, with good management and good luck, and an early investment in training pays dividends. Individual animals can be trained to a far greater extent than people realise, whether in the interests of easy handling or to perform a task of some kind. If you have only a few cattle, take time to get to know their individual abilities and inclinations and then train them by exploiting their talents. You might well revise any generalised prejudice about cows being obstructive and stupid, and you might even find a new and useful role for cows.

In the interests of all, encourage social harmony in the herd by keeping stabilised social groups together at all stages if possible. If dry cows are separated from the group, at least keep them adjacent so that they can maintain social contact over the fence. When introducing new cows to the group, keep them too in an adjacent area so that the initial meetings can be safely conducted – though even then there is bound to be a fair bit of pushing and shoving when the new animal actually joins the group.

In a seasonally-calved milking herd, try and ensure that heifers calve before older cows so that they can get used to parlour routines before they have the added stress of mixing with their elders. It is important that the heifer's first experiences of the parlour are good ones and it is worth letting her come in regularly for quite a while before she actually calves. Be consistently patient and gentle with her or you will end up with a nervous, spooky cow who will probably be a kicker. She will be nervous enough after calving for the first time anyway, not only because of hormonal changes and the strange new physical experience of parturition but also because she has been separated from her calf and that, of course, is a highly traumatic experience for any mother.

Avoid isolating any animal unless contagious disease makes it imperative. If possible, give her at least one acceptable companion if she has to be removed temporarily from her social group, and make sure it is an animal she gets on well with. Nor should a housecow be kept alone: give her a grazing companion, preferably one of her own kind.

HERDING

Cows resent being hurried: it is not their style unless there is a panic. The essence of a cow is ambling and ruminating. If you are trying to round up a group, it is usually best to be a leader rather than a herder (herders are predatory): cattle often follow out of curiosity and quickly learn to respond to a familiar call, especially if trained to do so by the rattle of a food tin. They will follow a familiar vehicle too.

Remember the flight space when you approach a wary group of heifers or bullocks; move towards them steadily and they will bunch together and stand there as long as you do not invade that crucial space. Use their curiosity: remain still, keep your eyes down, and let them come to you. Young animals are naturally inquisitive about unfamiliar objects in familiar surroundings (or vice versa) but at first they will be hesitant. They will only approach if they feel no apprehension. Watch their heads for a clue as to their intentions. Position yourself in such a way that the group's natural leader will move in the direction you want. It is not usually either necessary or desirable to herd with a dog, and the very presence of one immediately puts cattle in the role of nervous prey, but if you have a really steady dog you can let it *lead* them: most cattle enjoy chasing a dog that is heading away from them but most dogs feel belittled in the role. Otherwise, use drover dogs at the rear if you must but only if absolutely steady and reliable.

Keep the group together at all costs, then they will move straight and true. If one or two make a break for it, there will be chaos – and they *will* break if you invade that flight space. If one animal does break from the group, or if one escapes from the field, *leave it*! Chasing it makes matters much worse. Either release other animals to join it, or ignore it altogether. Its main aim will be to rejoin its social group and it will do so in due course if it is not harassed.

If active herding is necessary, make your arms seem longer by carrying sticks or branches which extend your presence and deter the animals from rushing past you. Leafy branches can be shaken to make a rustling sound that is equally a deterrent from passing you and an incentive to get moving in the opposite direction. The hiss of an aerosol tin sometimes has the same effect, as does a good imitation of the buzzing of gadflies.

Never use a stick to hit an animal. It is quite unnecessary to inflict any kind of physical punishment and will only make the animal less manageable in future.

Cattle are alarmed by unfamiliar slopes, however slight, and feel more sure of themselves moving up a slope than down one. They like a secure footing; they are very wary of the surface on which they tread and can panic at slipperiness or sudden changes in texture. They may also baulk at minor anomalies like drainage channels and shadows. And they have that wide range of peripheral vision which makes them as jumpy as unblinkered horses if they detect distractive movements or objects to one side; nor do they like entering dark places.

LOADING AND TRANSPORT

Like any animals, cattle are quick to sense that something is amiss and are deeply suspicious of unusual events and circumstances. Being loaded into a trailer or cattle truck definitely gives good reason for suspicion. If you intend to show your animals it is essential that loading and transport are rehearsed regularly so that, on the day, the events are routine rather than traumatic. The stress of the journey will otherwise be obvious in the show-ring, however carefully they have been brought to a peak of condition. They should be familiar not only with the loading routines but also with the enclosure in which they will travel and it might help to leave the trailer in the field for a few days to let them explore it at leisure before they are ever confined in it.

With small batches of market-bound cattle, especially from different social groups, keep them together in a holding pen for a week or so and then load direct from the pen. Keep the lorry out of sight of the queue until the last possible moment by making use of a curved race (see Chapter 4). Use the race to check, identify and weigh them as well.

Whether you have a couple of animals or a good-sized herd, it will make life easier for everybody if you devise or invest in equipment which facilitates catching and loading. However familiar the routine, few animals actually look forward to being confined and fewer still like entering a small, darkish enclosed space like a trailer, so you must take every possible measure to ensure the minimum of stress. Always allow plenty of time for loading: it is better if the cow can go at her own idle pace. The more you hurry her, the more determined she will be to stay free.

Ramps should only incline gradually and must give a good foothold (ashes and sand might help, and straw is a good disguise). Use funnelling of some kind to guide the animal towards and up the ramp almost without her noticing it. Open-sided channels like hurdles and railings may be easiest to manoeuvre but they can be distracting for the cow, whereas a solid panel rising above eye level will act as blinkers and will also reduce the risk of injuries like getting a leg between railings in a panic.

That beloved rattling food tin is the surest lure of all and if you proceed at an unhurried pace (and have a personal exit door open and ready for you in the trailer) you can act as leader and walk a slightly greedy cow quite readily up the ramp. Some sweet hay is another tempter. If a cow is properly halter-trained, so much the better for loading.

If gentle tactics really have failed and you are not inclined to give the whole business a rest until the animal is quieter again, there are a few tricks you can try as a *last* resort to move an animal. They are undignified for the cow and slightly brutal. You can lead her by the nose: grip the inside membrane of the nostrils between finger and thumb and pull her along, being very careful up the ramp and keeping her head well up (if the head goes down, so does the cow, and down she will stay). This grip can be surprisingly effective but to excess it can lead to bleeding and in any event it will certainly not relax the cow: the membranes are tear-jerkingly sensitive and your fingers will also impede her breathing, which could cause panic. A jaw grip is kinder, and very effective on calves in particular.

You can heave her in from behind with a rope against her rump and a strong pair of arms at either end of it. Or you can put pressure on her tail root by carefully beginning to coil the tail: hold it halfway down and begin to create a flat circle against her rump, or pinch the base of the tail. This will propel her forward at a steady pace.

The tail is a useful aid to keep a cow stationary as well, perhaps for veterinary attention. Hold it closer to the root than to the tassel (too low and you could break it) and hoist it into an almost vertical raised position.

RESTRAINTS AND HALTERS

Whether or not you intend to show them in the ring, all your cattle should be halter-trained to some extent. It makes handling so much easier for you and more acceptable to them on the odd occasion when they need to be restrained or led. Stall halters, incidentally, should be attached to fixed objects by means of a quick-release knot in case the animal falls.

Ideally such training should start very early in calfhood, before the animal realises it has the strength to defy you. A young child often makes a good trainer with a very young calf but an older calf can be surprisingly strong and a year-old heifer is certainly capable of dragging a hefty adult right across the field, grimly hanging onto the end of the rope. Once an animal knows it is stronger than you are, you have lost.

At that stage it is much better to let something firmly inanimate take the strain and the blame. Tie the lead to a very solid fixture and leave the animal to argue with the arrangement for perhaps half an hour a day for several days. Its anger at restriction will be directed to the object and you will come as a welcome relief when you arrive with food and kind words. A rub on the back will relax an unhappy heifer no end, and a blindfold calms a jumpy cow. You should take advantage of the animal's restriction to befriend it thoroughly, and grooming and conversation are useful allies in establishing a good relationship.

Another possibility is to let an experienced animal do the training for you, partly by example (though this works better with sheep and dogs than cattle) and partly by tying the two animals together so that the trainee is bound to follow the movements of the mentor, who should be the larger animal. However, some people successfully use donkeys in this role!

THE RECALCITRANT COW

Cows can be perverse, especially if you have upset them (in which case stand well clear of the dung and urine which will automatically be expelled). Sometimes they can be perverse for no apparent reason, though usually your own failure to read some social signal or your deliberate ignorance of that signal will be the trigger for awkwardness. You may be the boss but it is only fair that you should try and respect the cow's natural codes of social conduct.

Cows are large, heavy creatures and can cause considerable damage quite unintentionally – by treading on your foot, by turning a horned head unexpectedly, by giving you a playful bunt, or (beware) by attempting to mount you when they are bulling. A deliberate head-on attack is rare but is a possibility if the cow is protecting a new calf.

Cows can also kick, usually in reaction to an irritation like a fly on the belly, an uncomfortable milking cluster or a heel-nipping dog. The most powerful part of the kick action is sideways and backwards. If you have a kicking milk-cow, there are a few remedies, but first of all find out *why* she kicks. She may have sore teats, or perhaps the machine's suction cups are too tight, or there is a slight electric shock through them. An inveterate kicker, who probably began with a bad experience and developed a habit, is likely to be much more trouble than she is worth. And it could even be personal: a cow could be a demon for you and an angel for someone else. Sometimes bad temper is simply in the cow's nature (this is rare, but do not breed from her) but sometimes it is not the fault of the cow at all.

The tail-lift will stop her kicking, or you could try the tedious method of milking with one hand and using the other to grasp her furthest hind leg so that your arm acts as a kick-bar. As a last resort, loop a rope around her

(a) The tail lift
(b) Anti-kicking device

waist just in front of the udder and haul it quite tight. There are various metal devices on the market which work on the same principle as the rope, applying pressure which seems to render the cow quite incapable of kicking. Pressure points also come in useful if you need to 'cast' a cow (get her down for veterinary attention) and there are ways of tying ropes which effectively paralyse certain muscles temporarily and bring her down.

HANDLING BULLS

However well you know a bull, be prudent in his company and always be on your guard. But do not be nervous of him – that is asking for trouble. If you lack confidence, do not go anywhere near him.

In theory, beef-breed bulls are placid, especially if running with their cows, but do not take that for granted. Dairy-breed bulls really do seem to be less trustworthy (often because they are kept alone except for occasional 'work') and should always be handled by two people, not one. Any bull can turn suddenly into an aggressive and powerful opponent and he will weigh a great deal more than you do, giving him a huge advantage in any battle of wills. What is more, if he does attack he *means* it and he will be surprisingly agile for his bulk.

Bear in mind that mature bulls are categorically territorial and it is both insulting and dangerous to move them from their own territory. At three years old a bull is beginning to mature and is starting to try and establish his status; he can be quite dangerous at this age, and even more so by the time he is, say, seven or eight years old. The majority of sexually mature bulls do exercise self-restraint: they will be bold but not mean. Another fairly large proportion are apprehensive and would rather flee than fight. A few are always aggressive towards humans; they will consistently threaten but rarely actually attack. And then there are the potential killer bulls, with high libido levels combined with a constant aggressive attitude to all and sundry. Threequarters of bulls who have attacked a human being once will attack again.

With experience you can tell a lot about a bull's mood from the way he holds his head. If it is down, with shoulders hunched, there will be a look in his eye that spells certain trouble: you might escape a charge if you back off out of his fight/flight space. A slight tucking in of the chin is a submissive attitude: you can almost see him backing off. A minor lift of the chin with a softer eye is often seen when a bull takes pleasure in being groomed, and, as usual, regular grooming does help build up a good relationship.

Remember that actual confrontation between two bulls is usually limited to a formal bit of head banging with little real damage in most cases, but a human being is nothing like as tough as the head of a bull and a formal or playful butt may be very damaging indeed, however friendly the intent.

A handler must be confident with the bull and must make it quite clear who is boss at all times. There is a maxim that if you unwittingly find youself in a field with a bull, get out; if you are not yet in the field, stay out. That is fine for ramblers. For handlers, it helps to carry a couple of sticks to present a larger visual image. If you do find yourself cornered, do not panic. Back away gradually to get yourself out of his fight/flight space (perhaps 6m radius) and watch him carefully until you reach the safety of a barrier. If you turn and run, you have had it: he will immediately give chase. In a field, if you do run make sure you go downhill – a bull can run very fast up a hill but finds a down slope more difficult.

A good dog is a handy back-up. There is many a dog who has rescued its owner from a rampaging bull, usually by distracting him with barking and snapping so that the victim can crawl to safety. Dogs, those faithful companions, will risk their lives for their unworthy owners.

Under the 1981 Wildlife & Countryside Act, you may not permit a bull to be at large in a field crossed by a right of way unless he is not more than ten months old or is *not* of a recognised dairy breed and is accompanied by cows or heifers.

IV

EQUIPMENT AND ACCOMMODATION

Those who are fortunate will already have well-bounded grazing and potentially useful housing for their cows. Those who do not will have to dig out their cheque books, their ingenuity and their latent building skills, and have a long think about fences, shelters and capital grants.

THE FIELD

In this context 'field' means enclosed pasture (permanent or temporary), rough grazing, commonland, free-range grazing on hills and moors, orchards for tethering – in fact, any land which is available for livestock.

The main features of a field are grazing (a good *mixture* of plants), water, shelter, varied landscape features and security. The latter is important and is completely under your control. The cliché about good fences making good neighbours is true, and time spent in the early days creating (and thereafter maintaining) sound, cattleproof boundaries will save much bad temper and short breath (or worse) later on.

Hedges

To remain stockproof, hedges need regular trimming aimed at bushing them out right down the the base, and periodic laying. Unlike sheep, who will squeeze themselves insistently through the most unpromising narrow gap in a hedge, cattle do not often barge out, and rarely crawl through, but they can find themselves on the wrong side almost accidentally when leaning into the hedge to browse a tantalising shoot just out of reach.

Permanent fences

First of all, find out about possible fencing grants. Then consider the type of fencing. Post-and-rail fences may not be ideal; they are expensive for a start and they need expert installation, especially if morticed. Nailed rails give way under pressure from bulky cattle; bullocks, heifers and even fully bagged cows *can* jump a rail if they panic at gadflies or the menace of an overhead hot-air balloon, and younger animals lying next to the fence may roll under the lower rail quite unintentionally in their dozing. A determined bulling heifer, or one addicted to orchard apples, soon learns to get down on her knees and shrug her way under the rail, though a strand of barbed-wire will put a stop to such adventures.

A barbed-wire fence is an admission of failed husbandry (what happened to your hedges?) but is relatively cheap, long-lasting and straightforward to put up. Posts are usually oak, chestnut or treated softwood, depending on your pocket and your land. Chestnut, if locally available, is half the price and will last at least ten or fifteen years (perhaps as many as thirty or forty) on a well-drained site. It is a naturally durable wood but is not suitable if your land lies wet for long periods. The strongest wood is the heartwood, and if the posts are made up from young, thin stems they will consist of far more sapwood than heart and will not last as well as split stakes made from larger diameter poles.

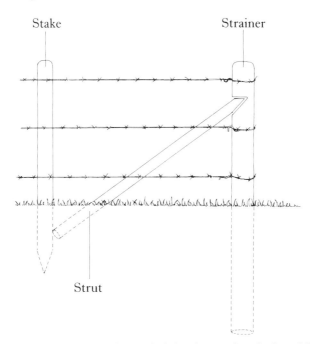

Stake   Strainer

Strut

Barbed-wire fencing: note that the first stake is hard up against the foot of the strut to give extra support

Treated softwood is claimed to have a life of perhaps twenty-five years, but you should be wary of the claim. For a start, the treatments have not been practised for that long yet so no one really knows if the claim is valid. Secondly, it depends on the thoroughness of the treatment. Slice the top 25mm off a treated post and see just how far into the wood the preservative has penetrated. To be fully effective, it should colour the wood virtually through to its core; it is useless if it merely stains the first 10mm.

Straining posts, buffered by struts, should be placed every 50m (100m at the most – preferably not more than 70m) as well as at corners and run-ends, and you need whole posts about 12–15cm in diameter and 2.1–2.3m long, dug in so that they stand about 1.2m above ground level. Cut notches into the strainers at about 0.9m high, and knock 2.4m struts sideways into them at angles, with the footings buried, along the lines of strain to wedge the posts against the considerable pull of the wire. The struts should be round poles about 7–10cm in diameter.

Strut notches on a strainer post

Pointed stakes about 1.7m long with 10cm butts (7.5cm for rounds, and at least 10cm for splits) are placed three strides apart between the strainers. Use a line to set them in dead straight runs – no curves or kinks, or you will never get the wire taut. They should be banged in about half a metre into the ground, all to the same level and plumb vertical in every plane.

The wire should run on the inside of the fence; thus when cattle press against it, the posts take the strain rather than the staples. For cows you should use three strands of two-ply, 12.5-gauge, four-point barbed-wire set at about 1.1m, 0.7m and 0.3m from the ground. The bottom line is optional if your cows are reliable and there are no youngstock in the field. The wire must be as tight as you dare make it: any cow can find her way between slack wires.

Bear in mind that a circular field is the least expensive to fence (though the most difficult!) and that a long, thin rectangle is more expensive than a square enclosing the same area of land. Think about it: you need more posts.

Gates and gateways

Don't be tempted to make do with strands of wire at field entrances or crumbling gates tied up with string: you will curse every time you go into the field, and curse even more if the heifers go for a Sunday walkabout and you are on your own trying to round them up *and* untangle the gateway to get them back in.

Wooden field gates need hefty gateposts and hinges. Galvanised metal gates are lighter. On a two-cow holding you could improvise with sliding rails and U-bolts, using coach bolts slipped into drilled holes near the rail ends to stop them being slid out every time a cow slips her head under for a good neck-rub. It is probably worth investing in a hard surface of some kind at gateways to avoid too much mud, and with housecows the area can double up as an outdoor milking bay and a holding pen if it is in a corner of the field.

Electric fencing

Ideal for temporary fencing, internal partitioning or strip grazing, electric fencing is not for property boundaries. It is, however, much the cheapest and most flexible form of fencing. Posts can be as much as 10–12m apart. The runs must be straight between corner posts so that the wire is properly stretched: slack wire is useless. You could use high-visibility electric fencing tape instead of wire if members of the public are likely to barge into the fence, and you should anyway put up warning signs for the public.

Put the top wire at about 0.75m or 1m above ground level. This is probably adequate for contented cows but young stock need a second strand lower down. Ensure that the wire is well insulated at all contact points and keep growth clear of it because otherwise some of the power will dissipate. Check at regular intervals; livestock will eat any grass they can reach under the wire but rain and wind could bend out-of-reach long grasses into contact with the wire. Also, wire stretches on a warm day and therefore sags.

Tether-grazing

Tethered cows are rarely seen on the mainland now but they used to be commonplace. Island cows in particular have a long history of tethering, often by means of a rope looped over their horns. It is an ideal way of making use of random areas of grazing where fencing is not possible – for example, on commonland, in an orchard, or along verges, headlands and greenways. Early training is essential and you must ensure that the cow has access to fresh water at all times, adequate grazing and, in hot weather, shade when she wants it.

Water

A grazing cow yielding milk can drink as much as 55 litres of water a day, especially in warm weather, and the higher her milk yield, the more she is likely to drink. An ample supply of fresh water is essential not only for her general well-being but also for a continuing supply of milk. Cows prefer not to walk more than 200m for a drink and if the trough is too far they reduce their frequency of drinking and their milk yield drops.

Cows like to be able to see around them while they are drinking. Remember that, in true bovine fashion, they tend to drink all together if there is room, or at least in fairly quick succession. The water trough is therefore a place with potential for social confrontation and tension, so allow maximum access space.

Ensure that ballcocks work efficiently and are housed out of cow reach. Insulate the trough and exposed pipework to avoid winter freeze-ups – a good thick jacket of turves packed around straw or manure is effective. Normal insulating materials are likely to be eaten by the cattle or at least pulled to shreds, especially by young animals who will try anything remotely edible.

A natural spring feeding a drinking and paddling pond is nice in theory but you need a concrete apron and ramp well into the water to prevent it becoming a smelly bog. You also need to ensure that the water is not contaminated from upstream sources or by underground seepage from septic tanks and agricultural run-offs.

Shelter

Cows do not on the whole object to the weather but they do try and avoid wind-driven rain by turning their rumps to storms or sheltering in the lee of a high hedge. Suckler herds on the hills are often run out all year and although they are hardy by nature they appreciate optional shelter of some kind. 'Dry back and dry bag' are the aims and a simple open-sided, roofed structure like a low pole-barn set in a sheltered spot, or an old open-fronted cart-shed facing out of the prevailing weather, will give a dry bed and protection from rain. A stand of trees gives shelter from snow and wind.

For a housecow or a handful of cows, it is worth building a field shelter – nothing elaborate but enough to make them feel more comfortable. With ingenuity it could cost very little, though it may not look very beautiful. A shed about 3m × 2.5m is adequate for one cow, and if you pave it (concrete or discarded pavement slabs from the local council) you could use it occasionally for hand-milking.

Field shelter at Hollanden rare breeds centre in Kent

Calf shelters

Most cows can calve happily in the field, and their calves are usually much the healthier for it. The young will need access to some kind of shelter, though they may not deign to use it if they are running with their mothers. Calves in a group on their own definitely need somewhere to escape from driving rain and cold winds and the simplest, cheapest structure is based on straw bales (if you live in the right part of the country), preferably covered with chicken-netting to prevent them being pulled to shreds. If you have larger livestock in the field, keep them away from a straw-bale shelter by erecting rails creep-fashion so that only the calves have access, because the older animals will use the bales as butting pads or scratching areas and could easily dislodge the whole edifice. Build the bales bondwise, supported by a few stakes, and give the shelter an open front and a roof.

HANDLING FACILITIES

The general concept of handling systems is to channel animals gradually into restricted spaces so that they can be inspected, treated or contained. The more gradual the funnelling, the less likely they are to object or panic.

So, you have an open field. The first task is to gather your cattle in a roomy collecting enclosure, then funnel them into single file in a race.

Animals in the race end up one by one in a crush or handling crate where they are individually restricted for close handling, and then released into a dispersal pen where the whole group gathers together again before being turned free or directed elsewhere. The sight of the rest of the herd waiting in the dispersal pen encourages the race queue to keep moving.

This basic handling system is infinitely flexible and can be adapted for any number of animals, from one or two cows to a herd. However small the herd, some kind of well-planned handling system is essential – even the friendly housecow needs to be restrained occasionally for veterinary attention or AI and, being an intelligent soul, she will read your mind on the day such affronts are due and she will make quite sure she keeps well clear of the situation, especially if she has already seen, smelled or heard the new arrival. In such circumstances she is not going to amble up willingly to your usual call and you will have to trick her into it somehow or other. That is when a handling system will come in useful.

In planning the system, bear the following points in mind.

Collecting area

Cows follow a recognised leader, who might usefully be trained to enter the handling system willingly. If the system is associated mostly with good experiences and is used regularly, it will be easier to collect the group for something less acceptable.

Funnel gradually: too quick a restriction may cause panic. To avoid jams, funnel down to an angle of perhaps 20 degrees and not more than 30 degrees at the entrance to the race. Have one side in line with the race: a double splay tends to encourage two cows to try and enter the race at the same time.

Races

The race sides should be about 1.5m high and in the range of 0.65–0.75m apart. The aim is to have just enough room for your largest animal to pass through but not enough width for any animal even to consider turning round. The bottom rail should be about 0.25m from ground level, with three rails above it (tubular metal or sawn timber, and no protrusions).

Curved, serpentine or angled races with sheeted sides encourage the herd to move forward. A straight race makes them only too aware of activity at the crush, but a deflected approach gives them the feeling of returning to the rest of the herd. However, cattle are bulky and do not bend easily in the middle, so avoid tight curves or corners or make the race wider at turns.

Crushes

Crushes or handling crates are designed to restrain one animal securely with minimal movement, and to give access to all parts of the animal for

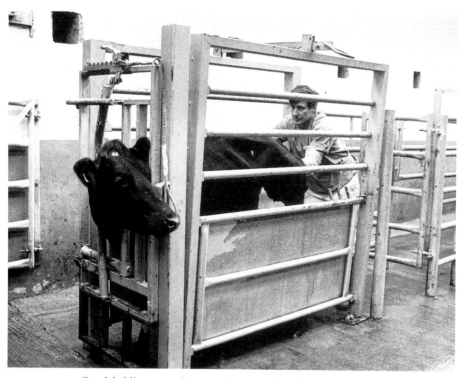

Crush holding a cow for an embryo transfer. [Farmers Weekly]

whatever treatment is intended. That includes its rear end and you therefore need a personal access gate for the handler between the end of the race (where the waiting queue remains) and the back of the crush.

Keep the animal in position with pressure from the adjustable sides of the crush, with or without some form of head yoke and with a barrier firmly against the back end to prevent movement back and forth. Yokes must have a quick-release system in case an animal slips and falls. Make sure the floor of the crush area is slip-proof, using ashes or sand if necessary.

HOUSING

As soon as you house an animal, you increase the risk of stress and disease. Design your housing in the best interests of the *cow*; too many people design cowhousing for the comfort and convenience of the cow handler who, except in rare cases, does not actually live in it. Thus the first rule must be: put the needs and preferences of the cattle well above those of their handlers.

The second rule is: simplify. All they really need is shelter, a dry bed, fresh air and good ventilation. In many cases, out of doors may be better than elaborate housing.

Many suckler cows never see the farmyard (unless the farmer finds it easier to visit them there). Beef cattle are usually wintered in yards or loose-housing, and dairy cattle systems vary from the relative freedom of yard-and-cubicle to the total restriction of tied stalls.

Cowhouses

The traditional cowhouse system confined milking cows to individual stalls in a building for the entire winter. The cow was tied with a chain which slid on a vertical pole to enable her to stand up or lie down. She did not often have the elbow room or chain length to groom her own flanks, however, and in fact almost every natural activity seemed to be denied her. She often spent most of the winter in darkness. She was fed and milked in situ and rarely had a chance to stretch her legs until spring.

Loose-house and yard

Cattle can be loose-housed in yards which are either partially or totally covered. There is a covered free-range bedding area on straw and an exercise and feeding area, covered or not.

Cows are commonly milked in an adjacent parlour with its own collecting yard accessible from the feeding area. Allow 3.7sq.m per cow in the bedded area plus a minimum of 1.8sq.m per cow in the feeding and loafing area, and the arrangement can accommodate anything from a couple of house-cows to a large dairy herd.

Management of the bedding may be somewhat laborious, which is one drawback of the system. The cows do not keep very clean and you will probably use about half a tonne of straw per cow in a typical 150–day winter. The cows seem quite content with this system and enjoy their freedom of choice.

The loose-house system is also popular for beef cattle, who sometimes have all their food brought to them rather than access to silage and hay in an exercise area.

Cubicles and cow kennels

More sophisticated than loose-housing is the use of individual cubicles built within a roofed building and arranged in rows on each side of a central access passage. The concrete-floored cubicles are raised by about 28cm and bedding requirements are substantially reduced because nearly all the dung falls into the passage, so that cubicle cows keep much cleaner than loose-housed ones. If the ground slopes slightly across the width of the cubicles, it encourages all the cows to lie on the same side and this avoids neighbours treading on each other's teats. The cows have complete freedom: they seem to like the privacy of a cubicle but are able to socialise at will, wandering down the passage to food and water in a separate area much as they would in the loose-house and yard system. The cubicles are about 2.1m long and 1.1m wide, depending on breed, and are divided by tubular metal or timber rails at 0.45m and 1m above the level of the cubicle floor. The lower rail could usefully be made of a more flexible material: sometimes a cow's leg gets trapped under the rail and could be broken by a solid one.

A cow kennel is a self-contained cubicle with its own roof and back wall (usually corrugated metal), standing on concrete or chalk and bedded with sawdust or shavings on a base of sand or rubble. The kennel system is extremely flexible: the cubicles are often built in batches, with a wall at each end of the batch so that every batch is in effect a building in its own right. They are ideal for small numbers of cows and you can always add a few more when your herd increases.

Bedding

Straw bedding in loose-housing serves two purposes: it mops up dung and urine, and it gives a comfortable, insulated bed. In cubicles you could use shredded newspaper, softwood sawdust or shavings (not chemically treated in any way), sand or straw. Chopped straw has advantages: it provides a drier, cleaner bed and is easier to handle than long straw. Sawdust or shavings might give rise to mastitis problems. Or you can use cow mats, which are pads of rubber, polyester etc. If bracken is used for bedding, bear in mind that it is poisonous when green and remains poisonous if cut green.

Housecow housing

The housecow owner's resources and available space are likely to be limited and it is usually a case of making the most of what you have – perhaps part of a barn, or an old cart-shed, or a loosebox or even a converted garage if it has natural light and enough roof height to give adequate ventilation. All a cow really needs is access to shelter when she feels like it; her owner, however, may find it more convenient to have her well under cover in winter both because people do not relish braving the weather and because the field will suffer if it is trampled in all seasons.

In general, your basic winter housing should have a covered bedding area, a feed/exercise area, and somewhere quite separate for milking, though more often than not a housecow ends up with one all-purpose shed in which she sleeps, cuds, feeds, drinks, calves, milks, evacuates, ambles and converses, and from which she escapes with glee at a gallop in spring.

Calf housing

Calves not running with their mothers are immediately at a health disadvantage. Calves in large batches are even more at risk, especially if their housing is in use continuously.

Ideally, calves should be kept in small batches of no more than five or ten, and kept in that batch all the way through with each group being totally separate from other groups in terms of the air they breath (many calf problems are respiratory). As each batch vacates its self-contained accommodation, you have a chance for a thorough clean-out and can give the area a good long rest before a new batch arrives.

Being a lying-out animal, a new calf actually appreciates isolation for the first few days and will be happier in its own private stall or pen, perhaps 1.2m x 1.8m and with solid sides. After a week or so, however, it, needs social contact with other calves. You can keep the calves in individual pens with open fronts so that they at least have face-to-face contact with each other. Loose calves in one pen together need 1.! sq.m of floor space per calf up to a liveweight of 135kg and the calves should all be about the same size. In crowded pens they show a definite preference for outer edges and corners, and the centre of the pen is often underused. It seems that the ratio of perimeter to enclosed area is an important factor, increasingly so the more crowded they are, but even a group of two or three tend to keep their heads to the perimeter and ignore the centre. Psychologically, the further they can see beyond the confines of the pen, the bigger the pen seems to feel.

Good drainage and a dry bed are important for calves. Try putting wooden slats on top of the concrete before adding the bedding. The housing must be draught-free but with adequate ventilation and ample fresh air. A constant temperature is more important than artificial heat, as long as the building and floor are properly insulated. Above all, hygiene is vital. There is a lot to be said for disposable units based on straw bales which can be burnt after use. Someone somewhere used to make heavy-duty cardboard pens for new calves and this might make an interesting diversification into recycled paper!

Bull housing

The essence of bull housing is that it should be comfortable, safe, and very robustly built so that he never learns just how strong he really is. It should be situated so that he does not sulk in perpetual exile: he needs to see, hear and smell all the activity – the cows going to the parlour, the people, the tractors, the cats and the dog going about their business. Let him feel part of the everyday life of the yard, even though he is restricted from social intercourse, because a lonely, bored, frustrated, under-exercised bull is a dangerous animal and unpleasant to know.

Soundly built yard for a Dexter bull

Give him a loosebox about 3.5m × 4.5m with a run twice as big (4.5m × 7.5m). The housing should be built in double brick or concrete blocks at least 230mm thick, with walls 1.7m high. The yard walls should be 1m high in brickwork, with solid pillars to full height to support three strong rails. The feeding manger should be sited so that the bull is fed from outside the box and you can get him used to the idea of restriction by yoking his head every time he feeds – a simple bar arrangement at the manger operated from outside by a lever.

The service crate should have direct access to his yard and could be built in one corner of it, where it can also be a bolt-hole for a harassed handler. If he is a big, heavy, aging bull, it is a kindness to his cows to build a ramp to relieve them of some of his weight but some bulls will not work in such undignified circumstances.

However much you love and trust your bull, be sensible. Remember that the pen is *his* territory and make quite sure that you have a means of escape, just in case, even if you bottle-fed him as a calf and cuddled him daily.

Isolation areas

If you have more than one animal you need extra accommodation against the day when an animal is ill, or due to calve, or there is some other reason for keeping it separate from the group for a while.

Cows for the Smallholder

An injured animal needs deliverance from bullying and from the risk of its injury being unwittingly aggravated by other cattle. A simple arrangement of gates can be used to section off a corner of a loosebox or yard for the patient: two gates, each hinged centrally on adjacent walls, can be used in any corner to make either a square or triangular pen, or one gate near a corner can make a treatment stall within a loosebox.

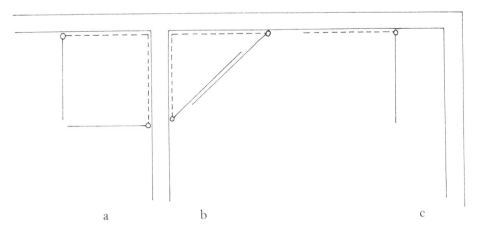

a   b   c

Using gates for instant isolation pens in looseboxes and yards. (The dotted lines show how the gates are positioned when not in use)
(a) Square pen from two gates
(b) Triangular pen from two gates
(c) Treatment stall from one gate

The cow kennel concept is useful for isolation accommodation and a large kennel, fitted with solid partitions instead of rails, would be suitable in many cases. For total isolation, however, you should invest in a separate, free-standing isolation box or shed, properly ventilated and insulated. It needs to be, say, 4.2m × 3.6m and 2.6m high. Bear in mind that it may be necessary to remove a carcase from it one day and so the doorway should be at least 1.2m wide, opening outwards.

A poly-tunnel could be a useful standby if you have nowhere else. It is an overgrown cloche clad with polythene and was originally designed for horticultural use. There are some new designs specifically for housing smaller livestock and they are cheap and easy to erect. They are not strong enough for numbers of cattle but would do for a couple of quiet cows for short periods if the sides could be protected. You would need to erect perhaps a makeshift pen of straw bales within the tunnel for a sick animal, and a calf would need a straw bale 'igloo' complete with its own roof and with no draughty gaps.

Loosehouse feeding: a Gloucester cow selects her fodder. The slanted rails allow each animal a chance to eat without being bullied

Food and water for housed cattle

A venerable wooden manger, polished by the tongues of generations of cows, is a pleasant asset but not very hygienic: it *could* be scoured out but rarely will be. Most farms use galvanised metal for food and water containers, which can be cleaned thoroughly, are light enough to be portable but heavy enough not to be forever in the wrong place. They come in all sorts of shapes and sizes and are long-lasting, cheap and easy to find.

Hay can be fed from racks or mangers at, above or below head height. If above, a lot of hay will be pulled out and wasted on the floor. Below head height (but above splash level) the cattle can make their selection within the manger and wastage should be less. Housecows can select their hay from nets. Silage feeding is dealt with in the next chapter.

Water is as vital for housed cattle as it is for those in the field and they must have unlimited access to fresh drinking water at all times. Even if you are operating on a shoestring with housecows, it will still pay you to invest in your watering system to avoid winter freeze-ups. Winter is always longer than the English, at least, expect and it comes round with amazing regularity every year. For some reason we are constantly taken by surprise by the facts of winter, whether we manage motorways, railways or cows. Be prepared: winter can bite!

Hygiene and health in housing

To avoid health problems, you basically need good ventilation, adequate insulation and excellent hygiene. Straw is a useful, cheap insulation material; it can be hung on wire netting above the animals' lairage and renewed at *regular* intervals so that there is no build-up of vermin or pathogens. You can also build complete housing units with straw bales, topped with a roof of corrugated sheets; they are not only cheap to make but can be completely renewed at intervals so that, again, there is no chance for disease to build up – ideal temporary housing in emergencies.

The principles of natural ventilation are these. Warm, stale air is lighter than cool, fresh air and it will therefore rise. As long as it has a means of escape, it can set up a simple circulating system whereby the stale air leaves the building at its highest point (perhaps an open ridge) and the fresh air is naturally drawn in to take its place as long as it has a means of entry, e.g. through baffled inlets at the top of the walls beneath the eaves, or through spaced boarding forming the upper half of the walls, which will also let in more natural light – highly desirable. Better still, the top half can be entirely open-sided.

Regular hygiene routines make a considerable difference to the health and welfare of your animals and save enormously on veterinary bills. All housing needs to be emptied of livestock periodically, scrubbed from top to bottom (in that order, starting right up in the roof), thoroughly disinfected and then rested. The longer an animal is housed, and the more animals there are under the same roof, the greater the risk of disease. Crowding will anyway increase general stress, which lowers all animals' resistance to disease, especially youngsters.

SLURRY AND MANURE

The housecow owner may well find that manure removal becomes quite a chore, as any shifting is likely to be done manually with fork and barrow. You generally have two options if you are bedding the cow. Either allow the bedding to build up to a good, deep, insulating layer with fresh straw on top as required (in which case the floor level rises during the winter and you should take this into account in designing railings etc.) and muck out as a major operation at the end of the season, when it will all be compressed into interleaving layers and quite heavy to handle. Or you can clear out very frequently, removing dung almost as it is dropped and forking out all the bedding perhaps once a week to replace it with fresh straw.

In cubicle systems, where there is little or no bedding to absorb dung and urine, you end up with wet slurry in the passages rather than humus-rich manure in the midden. It is easy enough to scrape the slurry away but then what do you do with the stuff? Here are a few facts about manure and slurry which might help.

A dairy cow weighing about 500kg will excrete perhaps 32–54 litres of dung and urine a day. A beef bullock weighing 400kg will produce 19–28 litres. The quantities are affected not only by the animal's size and diet but also its breed: a Holstein cow excretes about 20% more than the average Friesian.

Excreta contain not just digested food residues and waste but also a mass of micro-organisms, including any pathogenic bacteria passed by a diseased animal. Slurry spread on the land may therefore contain infectious organisms, particularly Salmonella bacteria. Beware of contaminating the grazing.

Slurry stinks and the longer you store undiluted slurry the more it stinks, especially if you stir it up and store it in anaerobic conditions. Slurry spreading stinks too.

Undiluted cattle slurry spread on the land in spring offers the next crop 1.5kg of nitrogen (N) per cubic metre (or up to 2.5kg if the slurry is incorporated into the soil soon after application, or much less if spread in autumn or early winter), 1.0kg phosphorus (P) and 4.5kg potash (K). Every 10 tonnes of properly stored cattle manure (see Chapter 10), spread in late winter or spring, provides 15kg N, 20kg P, 40kg K and organic matter to improve soil structure.

Slurry tanks are dangerous. They can drown animals or children. They can give off poisonous, inflammable or even lethal gases, especially in confined spaces. Their contents can pollute watercourses and create public health hazards.

Slurry can be treated to reduce odour, to reduce BOD (biological oxygen demand, a major factor in water pollution), or to produce energy (methane or bacterial heat) which can be used.

Farm effluent

Farm effluent includes that from slurry, manure, silage (lethal to water-life) and parlour washings. Farm drainage of all kinds is classified as trade effluent which may not be discharged into any watercourse, directly or indirectly, without the consent of the water authority. The authority *must* be consulted in the early stages of designing any livestock system: it is much better to be on good terms with them and to get everything right from the start, rather than cause trouble to downstream neighbours and be prosecuted later.

A final thought: sixty years ago salmon teemed and Tarka the otter hunted and played in the clear waters of the River Torridge in North Devon. Thirty years ago a farming revolution began in the West Country and rough grazing was improved by conversion to permanent pasture on a large scale. Today there are about 84,000 cattle and 140,000 sheep in the Torridge catchment area, producing enough effluent to represent a city. Farmyard slurry and silage run-off have found their way in quantity into the Torridge and in just the last five years it has been changed from a top-class pure watercourse to a class 3 river so polluted that long stretches of it are quite devoid of fish life, with not an otter in sight.

PARLOURS AND DAIRIES

Whether you have one housecow or a small dairy herd, you need an area used only for milking and also a separate area for dealing with the milk. That is a basic requirement of the Milk & Dairy Regulations, the aim of which is to ensure, for reasons of public health, that any milk offered for sale is milked out of the cow in the most hygienic conditions possible and is immediately cooled and stored in a separate room. And if it is good enough for the health of the public, it is good enough for the health of your own family in relation to the housecow milk they consume.

Parlours

The basic essentials of any milking parlour, however humble, are above all that it should be hygienic, and that it is attractive and comfortable for the cows. They will only milk well if they are relaxed and generally pleased with life. It also helps, in the parlour much more so than in the housing, if the milker's needs are catered for as well, because a good-tempered milker is happier with the cows and the cows respond to that mood. Music in the parlour is really more for the benefit of the milker, and only indirectly for the cows, who relax because the milker relaxes. Music also reduces the impact of background noises like clanging gates, buckets and swearing which can easily unsettle a cow.

For hand-milking, the best receptacle is a stainless-steel bucket – noisy, expensive and heavy but far more hygienic and long-lasting than a scratched plastic one – and a churn into which you can transfer pailfuls of filtered milk as necessary. Udder-washing equipment, at its most basic, can be a bucketful of hot water and a clean, disposable cloth or an udder-wipe. Cloths must be very clean indeed, boiled between milkings, and ideally not shared between cows in case one has mastitis or some other infection.

With a few more cows it is worth investing in a milking machine. In theory, practised milkers can hand-milk perhaps seven cows in an hour but a machine could come into its own if your herd is more than four or five. Milking machines speed up parlour routines, they are easier for your holiday stand-in to learn than hand-milking, they usually allow you to milk more than one cow at a time, and they transfer milk straight from the teat into an enclosed container with no contact with the outside air, reducing the chance of contamination as long as the system and the teat are immaculately clean.

On the other hand machines are expensive, they must be properly maintained, there are endless nooks and crannies that are havens for bacteria, they distance you from the udder, and they can (and too often do) abuse the udder. Mastitis is rife in many dairy herds and very often the machinery is to blame, directly or indirectly. Machines might also be responsible for undetected problems like the emission of high-pitched sounds inaudible to humans but unsettling for the cows.

Most milking machines use a vacuum to convey the milk away from the teat, combined with a pulsating mechanism which massages the teat by alternately creating and releasing pressure. The pulsating action is transmitted to the teat by a rubber-lined teat cup and the normal rate of pulsation is 60 cycles per minute.

For cows the equipment has four teat cups so that the whole udder can be milked at the same time. The four cups and the 'claw' which holds them are combined as a 'cluster' from which a single tube leads to the milk collection system. Each cluster also has an input line for the vacuum system.

There are, of course, many variations on this basic theme but their weak points are fairly similar. To work efficiently, they must not only draw the milk away from the udder but must also be comfortable for the cow in all respects. Many are not, largely because of lack of maintenance or because the cluster is left too long on the poor old cow – which hurts her, especially when she has given all her milk. To avoid being hurt, she may learn to let her milk down more slowly and thus prolong milking.

Machines can be powered by electricity (mains or battery) or petrol. The cheapest unit is the mobile vacuum pump with one or two enclosed 'buckets' and milking clusters. The capacity of the container limits the number of cows you can milk efficiently because you need to empty it into a larger churn at intervals (it usually holds up to about 25 litres). Mobility may be limited by the weight or bulk of the engine which drives the vacuum pump: it is often on some kind of trolley and some makes are easier to trundle around than others. Some have stainless-steel bucket units; some have transparent graduated jars so that you can check yields as you milk. Some systems give complete flexibility with mixed livestock; you can alter the vacuum pressure and substitute different types of clusters to suit sheep or goats as well as cows, or even camels if you want.

The bucket system can be tapped into a vacuum line fixed overhead permanently in a cowshed, but the buckets still have to be emptied by hand at intervals. A more sophisticated system for commercial dairy herds has a permanent pipeline which carries the milk from the clusters either direct to a bulk container or via graduated glass recording jars. Pipeline systems include built-in wash lines for cleaning the system thoroughly after each milking session – and do remember not to flush the cleaning water straight into a bulk tank full of milk! Portable bucket systems, on the other hand, have to be hand-washed.

A portable milking bail is a shed on wheels fully fitted with milking

Cows for the Smallholder

Portable milking bail for Guernsey cows tether-grazed on one of the island's golf-courses.
[Jane Archer, Farmers Weekly]

equipment. It can be taken to the cows in the field, rather than the cows having to waste energy and grazing time by coming into the yard.

If you are milking on a small scale, the capital cost of new milking machinery is alarming (see Appendix). It is possible to buy secondhand machinery, but beware! You may not be able to find replacement parts for it and you certainly will not have support from the manufacturer's agent when your system crashes and you have a dozen cows waiting to be milked. Try and buy reconditioned units from a reputable specialist dealer rather than chancing your luck at a farm sale.

The layout of a parlour for a small herd should be designed to ensure that the cows can 'flow' through the system easily. Herds of up to perhaps forty or fifty cows will be adequately served by a simple abreast system, which could probably handle the lot of them in an hour.

Given the choice, cows usually volunteer to be milked in more or less the same order every time, in a favourite stall. There is no point in trying to force a cow into a stall she dislikes. Get down to cow eye-level and imagine yourself with her bulk, her awkwardness and her innate fear of predators. Find out what spooks her, then change the stall accordingly if you can. It may well be something simple like shadows, or too tight a turn into or out of the stall, or it may be due to a bad experience in that stall in the past,

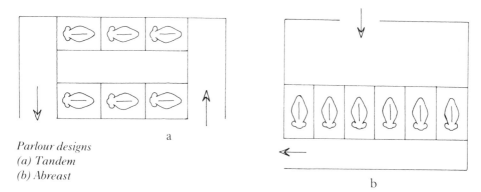

Parlour designs
(a) Tandem
(b) Abreast

perhaps when she was a first-time heifer, in which case you neither can nor should press the matter. An unhappy cow not only splatters the parlour with dung and urine but is also quite capable of withholding most or all of her milk.

Udder washing for more than a handful of cows needs a more sophisticated system than buckets of hot water. For example, there are systems which spray jets of water at the udder, or systems that have a rubber brush at the end of a hose to scrub the udder clean (gently!). Just as important is a system for sluicing away dung and urine, preferably immediately, either with a yard broom or scraper and hose or with a power hose.

The parlour and dairy should be sited so that the milk tanker has easy access to the bulk tank and the feed lorry can deliver bagged food to a store close to the parlour (you don't want to hump sacks very far). You need a collecting area for cows waiting their turn in the parlour and a dispersal area for those who have been milked. Site a water trough in the dispersal yard because dairy cows habitually have a drink after milking.

Dairy
The milk-room should be adjacent to the parlour but with a door between. Since 1979 all dairy farmers selling milk to the MMB have been required to install refrigerated milk tanks; the friendly days of the churns standing on a shaded wooden platform at the end of the track are gone. The tanks are stainless steel with capacities between 270 and 9,000 litres and new ones represent a sizeable capital investment. However, since the introduction of quotas many secondhand tanks are available. Most tanks use about 1kW of electricity for every 45 litres of milk cooled, or can be twice as efficient if a heat-exchanger is used to pre-cool the milk before it is put in the tank – perhaps something as simple as cold, running spring-water. You can then use the warmed water for other purposes, which is a satisfying recycling of energy.

If you are processing your own milk, you could use an in-churn cooler instead of a bulk tank. Your dairy will be under the watchful eye of the local ADAS dairy husbandry adviser; in addition the local council environmental health officers will take test samples of your products from any retail outlets. Dairies must be sited at least 18m away from dung heaps, cesspits and the like, and you might try the traditional trick of having a cool blue interior to deter flies.

Do not be tempted to use the family kitchen instead of a proper dairy: it is against the law. You will be in trouble in no time with blocked drains and with the water authority, and the public health people will rightly be on you like a shot for handling dairy produce in an area where other foods are stored and prepared (milk easily absorbs taints, odours and bacteria) and where family pets and children spend half their lives. To make any kind of a success of dairying enterprises, however small, be professional and keep them quite separate from the domestic situation.

V

FOOD AND FEEDING

A cow has four stomachs. The largest is the *rumen*, in which roughage is stored during active foraging and partly broken down by enzymes before being regurgitated in the form of a cud to be physically broken down by chewing at leisure (anything from 30–60 chews per cud), giving a greater surface area on which bateria can then act when the cud is swallowed again. If you watch a ruminating cow, you will see the shape of the well-chewed lump being swallowed and another lump coming up the throat for chewing a couple of seconds later. Rumination is a vital part of the cow's life, taking up quite a lot of her time.

All the activity in the rumen produces large quantities of gas from fermentation and so the cow belches – in the most inoffensive manner. A healthy cow's breath is as fresh as spring air and new-mown hay.

The rumen is huge: it takes up about 60% of all the cow's stomach space. It is designed to cope with cellulose and lignin, substances which humans cannot digest at all and which are major constituents of grassland plants. Coarse grazing takes some time to be broken down by the rumen microflora but non-fibrous, concentrated foodstuffs ferment quickly.

Sometimes a cow will ingest something basically inedible and this will be diverted into a much smaller stomach, the *reticulum*, where it can remain forever if necessary, but where there is considerable bacterial activity to degrade any dietary protein. The rough lining of the reticulum will be familiar to you as tripe, and butchers have found all sorts of strange objects inside it, like nails, wire and other hardware.

The third stomach is the *omasum*, which continues the digestive processes, grinding the fermented food to a paste and removing much of the water before it passes into the fourth stomach, the *abomasum*, which is the real gastric stomach where pepsins break down proteins to amino acids. The abomasum is the equivalent of the single digestive stomach in humans, pigs and other non-ruminants.

The balance of microflora in the rumen is complicated and is partly maintained by the fact that the cow, as a grazing animal, tends to eat frequently rather than to stuff herself hugely at widely spaced intervals like meat-eaters. Sudden changes in diet, or the sudden consumption of large

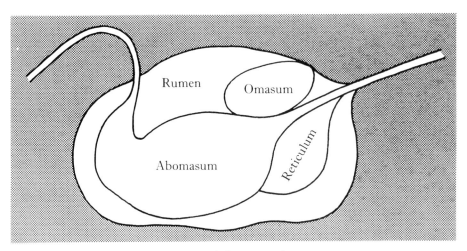

The cow's four stomachs

quantities of carbohydrates, can have a drastic effect on rumen acidity, and adequate roughage (cellulose etc.) and degradable protein are essential to its proper functioning.

NUTRITION

A cow takes in food with her tongue, which she curls round the plants so that she can draw them into her mouth and tear off their top growth with her tongue and lower teeth. She has no upper front teeth at all: there are four pairs of incisors in the lower jaw and they meet a hard dental pad on the upper jaw. The back teeth are well developed (top and bottom) for grinding the fibrous matter that forms such a large part of her diet.

A cow grazes selectively, using her eyes and her senses of smell and taste to identify the choicest growths. She has personal preferences as to species of plant and its stages of growth, and she definitely avoids coarse or hairy-looking plants or those contaminated by dung and urine. Some cows can detect trace elements and minerals in food and adapt their selection to counteract any imbalances in their diet but most do not, even if given free access to the required minerals.

Most cattle seem to prefer a salty taste to a sour one, and glucose rather than acid, and some vets swear that they all love the flavours of molasses or aniseed, often added to rations and drenches to encourage appetite. Wetter foods are generally favoured over dry ones and milking cows, given a free choice, often prefer silage to hay, and green fodder or roots to protein foods.

The three main categories of cattle food are *roughages, succulents* and *concentrates*. Roughages are dryish, high-fibre bulk foods like hay and straw. Succulents have a high moisture content, are very palatable and slightly laxative – foods like roots, kale, cabbage and silage. Concentrates have a high percentage of dry matter, are quickly digested and are rich in carbohydrates (e.g. cereals) or protein (e.g. fishmeal, oil-seed cakes, legumes) and are often relatively expensive.

The nutritional requirements of a cow are calculated to take account of two factors: maintenance and production. *Maintenance* basically keeps the cow alive and functioning, while *production* allows for growth, milk and the developing foetus. Maintenance rations are usually given in the form of cheaper bulk foods – grazing, hay, silage, roots etc. – and are often fed to the whole herd at the same rate or *ad lib*. If these foods are of high quality, they can also contribute to the production ration and effect cost savings.

Higher level production rations are commonly fed in the form of more expensive cereal-based concentrates given individually according to milk yield or liveweight gains. Concentrates have become necessary for modern cows because they are bred to produce such unnaturally large quantities of milk that their stomachs simply do not have room for the sheer volume of bulk foods needed to meet their nutritional requirements and sustain their yields. Too high a diet of concentrates can lead to health problems.

The ration is also calculated to give a healthy balance of the major constituents of food: proteins, energy factors (oils, fibre and carbo-hydrates), vitamins and minerals.

The weight of any constituent food in a mixed ration is calculated on the basis of its *dry matter* content (DM%). Succulents have a high water content and in fact a non-milking cow could go with very little to drink for several weeks as long as she had enough succulents to eat. Swedes, for example, have a dry matter content of only 10%.

Another factor to be considered is the *digestibility* of the ration, i.e. the proportion of energy in the food which can actually be absorbed and used by the cow as against the part which is wasted and excreted. The digestibility of forage is measured as the content of digestible organic matter within the dry matter content of the food, and the digestibility factor is known as the food's *D-value*. The D-value is a way of assessing the quality of grazing, silage and hay.

The vital factor to be taken into account is the *metabolisable energy* (ME) of the food. This is expressed in megajoules (MJ) per kilogram DM and gives an idea of how much energy the food can supply to the cow. Of recent years it has become the most important measurement in ration formulation.

Are you still there? Here's another factor – the cow's *appetite* for the food. It is no good devising a beautifully balanced ration with just the right amount to meet her maintenance and production requirements (or rather

Cows for the Smallholder

the production *you* demand of her) if she either has no room for the stuff or does not like the taste of it anyway. So taste and texture come into it as well – and of course comparable costs of different foods, and the availability of those foods, are other considerations.

It is little wonder that several agricultural software houses have produced ration formulation programs for computer users. It can be quite an enjoyable exercise even on the back of an envelope and you can look up D-values, ME values and the constituent elements of various foods in tables. Some of the more common feedstuffs are listed and analysed in the Appendix and the rest can be found in publications like the MAFF's *Energy Allowances and Feeding Systems for Ruminants*, which could be a mathematicians's delight.

There are some more factors to consider before you can devise the perfect rations. For example, apart from the cow's output you must consider her oestral or pregnant state (see Chapter 6).

Then there is her own breeding to consider. Some cows are better food converters than others, and that is genetically determined. Genetics affect whether she transfers her nutrition to her bag for milk or to her own back to get fatter.

And you still have not booted up your computer? Well, farmers have done without computers for centuries quite happily. In the past they did not demand such high returns from their cows. Today cows are bred and fed for maximum yields (no wonder they have health and stress problems) and unless you are desperate to make your fortune you will not need to get quite so complicated about rations. It helps to know something of the theory, but what it really boils down to can be summed up in figs. i–iv on the following pages.

A well-balanced diet gives adequate roughage for rumen functions, adequate water (in the food itself and for drinking) to keep tissues healthy and to replace liquid lost in milk production, adequate and balanced levels of protein, energy elements, vitamins and minerals – all mixed together in quantities which take account of the size and breed of the cow and the demands being made upon her. Once you know her basic requirement in metabolisable energy terms, the rest follows quite easily. Your aim is to combine various weights of different foods until you achieve a balanced ration in terms of ME and digestible crude protein (DCP) which meets the needs of the animal, and ensuring that the cow's capacity for that ration is adequate and that the ration is palatable and attractive to her. Take a look at fig. v (a) – (d).

And on pages 76 and 77 in fig. vi are some straightforward basic rations for cows, taking as examples the two extremes of Jersey (small cow, rich milk) and Friesian (big cow, big milk yields).

There is a simpler way of working out rations for *low* productivity

Continued on page 78

Fig. i FOOD

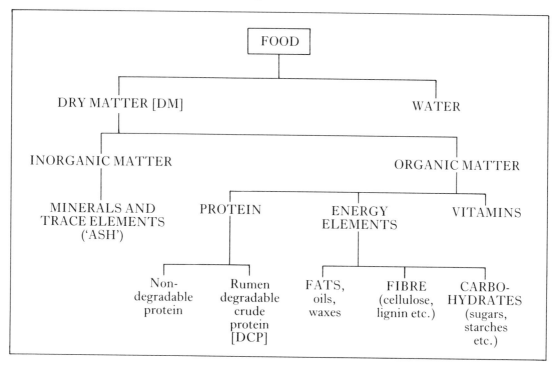

Fig. ii RATION FACTORS

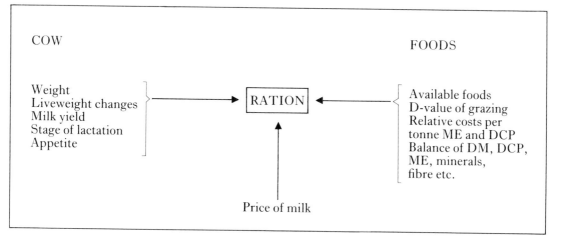

Fig. iii FOOD ENERGY

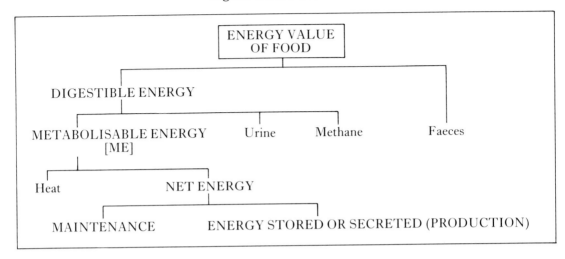

Fig. iv COW'S USE OF RATION

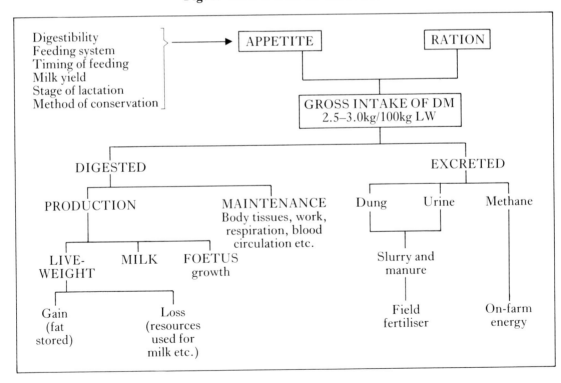

Fig. v

(a) DAILY MAINTENANCE ALLOWANCE BASED ON BODYWEIGHT

Bodyweight	*MJ/cow*
100kg	17
200kg	27
300kg	36

Bodyweight	*MJ/cow*
400kg	45
500kg	54
600kg	63

(b) DAILY PRODUCTION ALLOWANCE BASED ON MILK QUALITY

Solids-not-fat (%)	*Fat (%)*							
	3.6	3.8	4.0	4.2	4.4	4.6	4.8	5.0
8.5	4.90	5.04	5.17	5.30	5.43	5.56	5.69	5.82
8.7	4.98	5.10	5.24	5.37	5.50	5.63	5.76	5.89
8.9	5.04	5.17	5.31	5.44	5.57	5.70	5.83	5.96
9.1	5.11	5.24	5.37	5.51	5.64	5.77	5.90	6.03

(c) APPETITE (kg/day): DRY MATTER INTAKE, mid/late lactation

Bodyweight	*Milk yield (kg/day)*				
	5	10	15	20	25
350kg	9.3	9.8	10.3	10.8	11.3
400kg	10.5	11.0	11.5	12.0	12.5
450kg	11.8	12.3	12.8	13.3	13.8
500kg	13.0	13.5	14.0	14.5	15.0
550kg	14.3	14.8	15.3	15.8	16.3
600kg	15.5	16.0	16.5	17.0	17.5

(d) BREED FEEDING

BREED	LIVE-WEIGHT (kg)	MAIN-TENANCE ME (MJ/day)	PRODUC-TION per kg milk (MJ/day)	DIGESTIBLE CRUDE PROTEIN (g)		APPETITE (kg DM)
				Maint.	Prod.	
Ayrshire	500	54	5.1	300	53	15
Dexter	300	36	5.4	200	58	9
Friesian	600	63	4.9	345	48	18
Guernsey	450	49	5.7	275	63	14
Jersey	350	40	6.0	225	63	11
Kerry	400	45	5.3	250	53	12
Shorthorn	550	59	5.0	325	48	17
S. Devon	650	67	5.5	365	58	20

Fig. vi EXAMPLES OF RATIONS

FRIESIAN COW: yielding 20 litres

    3.2kg hay
    30kg silage
    8kg concentrates
    1.5kg sugarbeet nuts

FRIESIAN COW: yielding 10 litres

    3.2kg hay   *or* 6.8kg good hay
    27.2kg silage   18kg good silage
    1.8kg concentrates   1.8–2.7kg crushed oats
                               3.1kg concentrates

FRIESIAN COW: yielding 5 litres

    14kg good hay
or 6.8kg good hay + 18kg kale or cabbage
or 4.5kg good hay + 3.1kg lucerne hay + 22.8kg mangolds
or 8.1kg good hay + 18kg mangolds
or 8.1kg good hay + 2kg dried sugarbeet pulp
or 8.1kg good hay + 6.8kg brewers' wet grains
or 8.1kg good hay + 10.9kg molassed grass silage
or 8.1kg good hay + 1.4kg barley meal + 0.2kg linseed cake

FRIESIAN COW: maintenance only

    8.1–9kg good hay
or 5.4kg good hay + 18kg mangolds
or 5.4kg good hay + 2kg dried sugarbeet pulp
or 4.5kg good hay + 1.8kg oat straw + 9.1kg silage
or 6.4kg good oat straw + 13.6kg silage

JERSEY COW: yielding 10 litres

    3.2kg hay + 20kg silage + 1.8kg concentrates
or 3.2kg hay + 25kg kale + 1.8kg concentrates

JERSEY COW: yielding 5 litres

    3.2kg hay + 20kg silage
or 3.2kg hay + 25kg kale

JERSEY COW: maintenance only

    6.4kg good hay
or 3.6kg good hay + 15.9kg mangolds

Fig. vi (*continued*)

BULLING HEIFER

Minimum of 0.9kg concentrates per day + hay and/or straw at 0.2–0.4kg per month of age.

Examples
JERSEY: 15 months   *JERSEY: 20 months*
3.4kg hay   7kg hay
1.0–2.5kg concentrates   1.0–2.5kg concentrates
Straw to appetite   Straw to appetite

IN-CALF HEIFER

JERSEY weighing 320kg: 4.5kg hay + 9.5kg silage
                                 or 4.5kg hay + 12.7kg kale

FRIESIAN weighing 510kg: 8.2kg hay + 9.5kg silage
                                 or 8.2kg hay + 12.7kg kale

BULL

For every 50kg liveweight, give 0.68kg hay + 0.68kg silage, and then give 1.8–2.7kg concentrates per day.

NOTES

A cow could probably eat about 45kg wet grass per day in summer.

Feed concentrates at approximately the following rates:
Channel Island breeds (4.5–5.0%BF)   :2.7kg per 5kg milk
Other breeds (3.5–4.0%BF)   :2.2kg per 5kg milk

On grass or silage, use the bulk feed to give maintenance plus 5 litres of milk, then feed concentrates.

For 1 litre of average milk, you could feed:
   0.7kg medium hay
or 2.1kg medium silage
or 2.8kg kale
or 3.5kg mangolds
or 1.6kg brewers' grains

animals, whether dairy or beef, and that is the *hay equivalent* (HE) system. It is based on a kilogram of good hay – hay of a standard that would be fed to a dairy cow at the rate of 0.9kg a day for every 50kg of her own bodyweight for maintenance. A low-yielding cow could also make milk on the hay if fed at the rate of 0.8kg of hay for every kilogram (or litre) of milk yield, over and above her maintenance ration. For example, a 550kg cow giving 5 litres of milk per day could be given hay as follows:

For maintenance – 0.9kg × 550kg/50kg = approx. 10kg hay
For production – 0.8kg × 5kg = approx. 4kg hay
Total ration = approx. 14kg hay

Very boring for her indeed! But the HE system lets you vary her diet by substituting other basic foods at certain rates (fig. vii).

Fig. vii HE EQUIVALENTS

1kg hay is the equivalent of:
   3kg silage
or 2kg good feeding straw
or 0.5kg cereals
or 4kg kale or cabbage
or 5kg mangolds or swedes

Thus for each kilogram of hay you could instead give her 3kg of silage. Perhaps you decide to give her 8kg of hay and the balance of the ration in silage, in which case she would have (14–8) × 3kg of silage, i.e. 18kg of silage. Her ration is therefore 8kg of hay plus 18kg of silage.

The HE system is a rough guide and only for low yields. You should still check whether the balances of protein, energy etc. are adequate and it is better to use the metabolisable energy system for higher yielders, particularly to reduce the bulk of their ration by using some concentrates.

Sucklers and beef animals are more straightforward than dairy cows. Sucklers are not required to pump out milk at such high rates and, being under far less stress in every area of their lives, their dietary needs are much lower and simpler.

And do all your animals a favour: give them a little variety in their diets but not too suddenly – introduce new foods gradually. Especially with dairy cows, find out what they really love and let them have a little now and then, purely for pleasure.

GRASS

Summer feeding is much simpler than winter rationing: grass can meet most (if not all) of the cow's needs, but it does require management.

Grazing on old-established pastures or on the hills offers her palate a range of tastes and textures but a diet of nothing but Italian rye is pretty dull for an animal whose natural lifestyle is a ranging one.

Grass is a growing, changing food which forms the basis of most cattle's diets. It has different food values at different stages of growth, in different soils, with different management methods and at different times of year, and these values vary again if it is conserved as hay or silage. On a smallholding or small farm the only way you will really make the enterprise pay is by making the most efficient use of your grazing, which can substantially affect the health and output of your cows and thereby your profit margins. Fig. viii will set you thinking.

Fig. viii MILK FROM GRASS

The nature of grass

Grass grows fastest in the spring, and has another surge later in the year around September. Spring grass is at its most palatable and nutritious but is low in fibre; late-flush grass is bulky but has greatly reduced value as food. Grass is at its best in full leaf, before it flowers and goes to seed. As the flower stems mature, they become increasingly fibrous and form an increasingly larger proportion of the whole plant, so that the overall digestibility of the crop is considerably reduced. Nutritional qualities begin to decline quite sharply by midsummer.

Managing grass

Grass can be grown as permanent pasture over a number of years, building up into a good sward with a comprehensive root system able to cope with drought, severe winters and the tearing method of a cow's grazing, and generally containing an interesting mixture of grass species and herbs offering a good spread of trace elements, textures and tastes and also a reasonably long period of growth as different species mature at different times.

Alternatively, grass can be grown as a temporary ley for much shorter periods (from one to five years). This system gives flexibility, and specific species can be sown to meet specific requirements. Choice of seed mixture depends very much on local conditions and you should consult a local seed merchant for expert advice based on knowledge of the area.

The major nutrients for grass or any other crop are nitrogen, phosphorus and potassium, generally referred to as N, P and K. Nitrogen exists in soil either inorganically as ammonium and nitrate ions, which are easily leached out and wasted, or as organic compounds which are usually retained in the soil but are not available to plants until the organic matter is decomposed and its nitrogen converted into inorganic forms. Phosphorus is reserved in the soil in the form of soluble and insoluble phosphates, and as a fertiliser it is applied as calcium phosphate, ammonium phosphate or basic slag (a byproduct of the steel industry). Potassium, familiarly known as potash, is naturally derived from mineral weathering and is applied as a fertiliser in the form of potash salts such as sulphates, chlorides, nitrates (saltpetre) and phosphates.

The acidity of the soil also makes a considerable difference to grassland and is best within a range of 5.5–6.5pH (see Glossary for an explanation of pH). Clover prefers a minimum pH of 6.0. Have your soil analysed every three years for its pH value (the controlled use of lime can correct acidity) and also for the levels and balances of nutrients and trace elements.

Phosphate and potash levels can be adjusted by straight application of each element or in a compound fertiliser (check the bag for proportions of each component). Manure and slurry are also major sources of soil nutrients, of course. Nitrogen is the element which really maximises the growth potential of the crop, often with dramatic results, but equally it can be overused, not only to the detriment of the crop and the soil but also with severe repercussions in pollution of watercourses.

Judicious applications of manures and fertilisers can greatly increase the yield of the grass crop and enhance its nutritional value at the same time, but too much nitrogen, especially combined with potash, will *reduce* the protein content of the grass on a dry-matter basis although it will increase the total volume of dry matter per unit area. That is to say, you will get a lot more grass (or hay or silage) but it seems to outgrow its own strength and each kilogram contains a lower proportion of nutrients in relation to fibre so that greater quantities are needed to achieve desirable levels of protein, carbohydrate etc. in the cow's ration. There comes a time when her belly is full before nutrient levels are reached.

Managing the grazing

Your aim in controlling grazing patterns is to try and achieve the near impossible: to match the needs of your cows to the fluctuations in grass growth and quality. With sucklers and store cattle the tendency is to leave them undisturbed as far as possible and let them graze where they will during the season, save for areas set aside for hay or silage (which can be grazed after the crop has been harvested). Uncontrolled continuous grazing at set stocking rates has drawbacks, whatever its scale: it tends to waste the spring flush for a start, and on smaller acreages it leads to a build-up of parasites, which is dangerous for young animals in particular. Grazing needs an occasional rest to break the parasite cycle and to allow the more delectable plants to recover from selective grazing. The sward should be restricted to certain heights and needs to be mechanically topped before it grows away and goes to seed or becomes very stalky and fibrous or is spoiled by trampling. An ideal height for continuous grazing is about 10cm. Dairy cattle, with their greater demands for quality in the diet, should have their grazing controlled either by rotation through a series of paddocks or by strip-grazing between portable electric fences.

Conserving the grass

Winter grazing offers little or no nutrition. Spring grass grows far too fast to be grazed fully, therefore excess spring growth is conserved for winter use by being made into hay or silage. Hay has a high dry-matter content, is easy to handle whether in bales or from the stack, smells pleasant and is the traditional winter fodder. Silage is more succulent; it is generally handled in bulk, mechanically harvested, and either eaten where it is heaped or forked (by tractor) to the manger. On most holdings there is a place for both hay and silage and it is often cheaper in the long run to hire

Fig. ix GRASS ENERGY

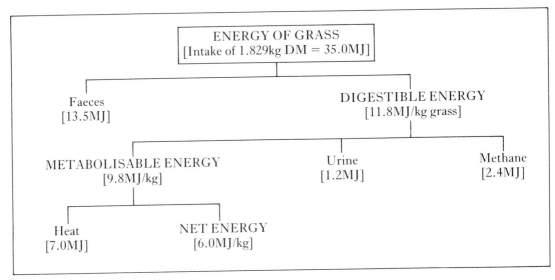

contractors to make either of them, especially silage. Then it is the contractor's capital which is tied up in the machinery, not yours. But of course the smaller your acreage, the harder it is to find a contractor when the moment is right for your crop.

Haymaking requires several consecutive days of fine weather; silage crops can be taken off the field within hours of cutting and only need part of a day with no rain and low humidity. Silage can usually be cut a month before hay.

The quality of silage and hay depends on the quality of the grass at the time it is cut as well as the efficiency with which the crop is conserved. In both cases, it is often worth sacrificing quantity for the sake of quality, but you can compromise by taking an early cut for quality and supplementing it with later cuts of lesser quality.

Top-quality silage is cut before ear-emergence; this not only gives the quality but also the chance to take two, three or even more silage crops during the season, or to have an early growth of aftermath for grazing. Hay should be cut before flower heads appear, when the crop is higher in digestible protein and starch but lower in fibre than hay cut in full flower. The early cut gives less hay, of course. In a good year you will get a second hay cut, though of much lower quality.

Cut grass continues to live for some time until it is dried or until it is deprived of air. By living, it begins to use up its reserves and thus dissipates some of the energy which would otherwise be made available to the cattle which eat the hay or silage.

Fig. x GRASS DIGESTIBILITY

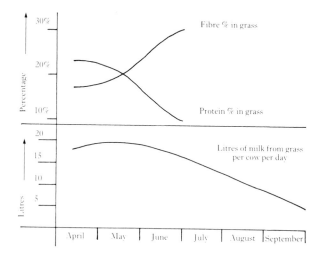

Fig. xi MILK FROM GRASS

Hay is preserved entirely by drying, preferably in the sun in field wind-rows turned and fluffed up at intervals to hasten the process and ensure even drying throughout. Made too slowly and overweathered, hay soon loses its 'nose', its palatability and its nutritional value; nutrients are too easily leached out by rain and dew and you can lose as much as a third of the protein of the original grass. You can also lose anything up to 20% of the dry-matter content of the crop between cutting and baling, especially if the swath is handled so violently that the dried leaf content is shattered. Just after cutting, moisture is lost rapidly even without any sunshine and the crop can be treated quite roughly, but the drier it becomes the harder it is to remove water and the easier it is to damage the crop. At that stage it does need sunshine, preferably with a breeze as well. Aim to reduce the moisture level of the grass to about 20% before the hay is baled and stored.

Silage is preserved by a pickling process. The green crop is fermented under acidic conditions with all air excluded. In well-made silage the predominant acid is lactic, with some acetic and very little butyric. The balance between these acids depends on the conditions in which fermentation takes place and is largely determined by the sugar and moisture content of the crop when it is cut. Sugar content depends on the type of crop and its stage of growth (for example, sugar levels are low in clover and in young grass) and can be improved by the use of special silage additives. Moisture content must be reduced to ensure good fermentation and also to avoid the risk of effluent seepage, which is both wasteful and a powerful pollutant in watercourses. Aim for a moisture content of 70–75%.

For high-quality silage, cut the grass when it is leafy, wilt it down to 25% DM within twenty-four hours, give an additive if necessary, pick it up in dry conditions (to avoid contamination by field soil as much as anything else), fill the silage pit quickly, then roll firmly, cover to make it airtight and seal it.

The aim in ensilaging is to exclude air. The smaller your heap, the greater its surface area with a potential risk of exposure to air, and the more careful you must therefore be to make sure the heap is properly sealed. The answer is to have some form of wall on three sides, lined with plastic sheeting – but beware of ripping as you fill. The lining should be of a size that it can be folded over the edges of the complete heap at the top so that there is a substantial overlap when a top sheet is in place. Floors should be cement if possible, with an excellent drainage system to a special tank.

Remove air from the heap by rolling and pressing – usually with the tractor – as you fill and before you cover and seal the heap. Finally, apply all-over pressure to the waterproof top cover by spreading a thick pile of wet grass on it, or a heavy layer of ground chalk, soil, sand or straw bales, or cover every inch with old tyres. Weight on top is important. Then leave the stuff to ferment until the cows are ready to use it.

Silage effluent must not drain into rainwater gulleys which lead to soakaways and thence to underground water supplies or watercourses: it can kill every fish for miles around because it is so full of dissolved organic matter which, on breaking down in the watercourse, makes huge demands on dissolved oxygen in the water and thereby deprives all other water-life of this vital gas. It can be truly devastating. Some people line the floor of the silage heap with a layer of straw bales to absorb effluent; they do take up a lot of space but the cows can eat the straw later. First and foremost, though, talk to your local water authority about where to site your pit or clamp and how to ensure that its effluent is properly handled. Silage effluent should be saved anyway and fed to livestock neat. They will probably love it and if you taste good silage effluent yourself you will know why – it is like sugar-water. In theory 13.5 litres of fresh silage effluent can be converted by the cow into 2 litres of milk.

Feeding hay and silage

A Friesian cow could give 15 litres of milk a day on 17kg of very high-quality hay (D-value 67, ME 10.1MJ/kg DM) or 5 litres on 13kg of the same hay. On hay of lesser quality, she will need concentrates as well. With moderate hay (D-value 57, ME 8.4MJ) she could be fed, say, 9kg hay and 8kg concentrates to yield 15 litres, or 6kg hay and 15kg concentrates for 25 litres. Good, well-made hay smells sweet and clean, with very little dust, and looks gently green and leafy rather than bleached and stemmy. A standard hay bale measures $0.9m \times 0.45 \times 0.35m$ and weighs about 20–30kg, so you will probably get 33–50 bales per tonne.

Silage with a D-value of, say, 68–78, can give you milk yields of 12–15kg a day, but an average silage is often barely good enough for maintenance, let alone production. High-quality silage might have a D-value of 68, ME 10.5MJ, dry matter 25%, whereas low-quality silage might have respectively 52, 7.6MJ and 18%DM. Every sample of silage (even in the same clamp) differs so much that it is difficult to suggest appropriate feeding levels and anyway you are likely to adopt the cafeteria method of feeding whereby the cows help themselves at the silage face, rather than cut it, weigh it and feed it individually. You can use the Hay Equivalent method to get a rough idea of how much silage to feed, but *ad lib* silage of good quality should give milk yields of, say, 10–12kg a day. Take care that the cow does not stuff herself so full of silage that she does not have any appetite for her concentrates or other rations. Keep the feeding face rough because it is much harder work for the cows to attack a smooth surface. Remember that, once exposed to the air, there is a possibility that the silage will begin to deteriorate if you give more face than they can keep up with. Control access to the face with an electric fence on a low setting. Bear in mind that silage is low in fibre, especially if made from early cuts; lack of fibre can lead to problems and can also reduce butterfat levels, so be wary of giving a cow nothing but silage and concentrates. Let her have at least 2–3kg of hay as well, especially if she is a high yielder.

A smallholder will no doubt stick to hay. It is easier to handle and easier to judge for quality and quantity, and there are no effluent problems. And you can easily fling half a bale of hay over the fence or string it up in a bag. Nor will any of your neighbours complain about the smell of hay, though they might object to silage, especially if it is made badly.

In whatever form the grass is consumed – fresh, as hay, ensilaged or even zero-grazed (cut in the field and carted to housed cattle for immediate feeding) – ensure that it contains no poisonous plants at all and, if possible, nothing which will taint the milk. Such plants are listed in the Appendix.

You can, of course, make hay and silage out of crops other than grass. For example, you could ensile brewers' grains, or chopped maize, or a mixture of home-grown fodder (cereals and pulses, or cereals alone cut just before the ear is shot). As usual, the cow-keeper has plenty of scope for ingenuity in making the most of what might be available.

VI

PREGNANCY AND BIRTH

A dairy heifer calf, especially one of the smaller breeds like the Jersey, can show signs of sexual maturity at as young as six months and it is always startling to see the little creature, barely out of calfhood, being flattened by the weighty attentions of older heifers and cows as they try to mount her.

On average, however, heifers do not reach puberty until they are perhaps eight months to a year old, or even a little more, and they are not normally mated until they are at least fifteen months old, and usually several months older. In a commercial dairy herd, heifers are judged to be ready for the bull when they reach at least two-thirds of their anticipated mature liveweight and this stage, like the timing of puberty, depends on breed, nutrition levels and general management as well as individual genetics. The average Friesian heifer, for example, might weigh about 60kg at two months old and be expected to reach a mature weight of perhaps 600kg, in which case she should not be put in calf until she weighs at least 400kg. If she is underdeveloped at calving time she is very likely to have problems with the birth, nor does it seem fair to put her on the production line so early in life. The gestation period is about nine months and, depending on how well she develops, it is perhaps best to aim for a first calf by thirty months old, which means getting her into calf by twenty-one months.

A heifer destined to be a suckler cow rather than a dairy cow is under much less pressure and is often not put in calf until she is perhaps twenty-seven months old, to calve down as a three-year-old.

Bulls mature a little later than heifers of the same breed. They are sometimes used as early as ten months old, but only very occasionally – they are not really worked with any regularity until they are at least eighteen months old. A bull's production of semen does not reach adult levels until he is about three years old.

THE OESTRUS CYCLE

A cow comes into oestrus for a fertile period of a few hours and she comes into oestrus again on average every twenty-one days, repeating the cycle until she is successfully in calf. Many cows are very regular: you can almost guarantee that they will be bulling every third Tuesday. Some have regular cycles a few days longer or shorter than the twenty-one day average and some are less regular altogether, with cycles of varying length each time but generally within the typical range of eighteen to twenty-three days, though some may be very much shorter – even as often as every eight days.

Heifers tend to have briefer heat periods than mature cows and individuals vary enormously: a heifer's season might last as little as an hour or two. About a quarter of all cows have heat periods lasting less than six hours in the winter, though they may increase to twenty-four or even thirty-six hours in summer.

The short-period animals are often called shy breeders. They are probably perfectly fertile but, unless they are running with the bull, no one notices that they are bulling and therefore no steps are taken to get them into calf. Some people use the term 'silent heat' but with a true silent heat the cow shows no signs of bulling at all, however brief, though she does release a viable egg.

Cows release a single egg in each heat and the egg will only survive for about eight hours if it is not fertilised. Ovulation generally occurs about ten to twelve hours after the end of the oestrus period and the timing of insemination is important. If it is too early, the fertility of the semen is reduced by the time the cow ovulates and the chances of conception are therefore decreased. It is better to inseminate towards the end of the heat period than near the beginning, and as a general rule a cow which is first seen bulling in the morning should be served during the afternoon of the same day, while a cow bulling in the afternoon should be served the following morning. It is common practice to inseminate problem cows on two successive days.

Fig. xii TIMING OF SERVICE

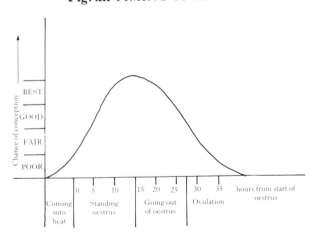

The most efficient aim is to calve a cow once every twelve months, and every calfless day beyond that period whittles away your milk income. An average gestation is about forty weeks, varying according to the breed of the *bull*.

Fig. xiii AVERAGE GESTATION LENGTH BY BREED OF BULL

Jersey	279 days
Aberdeen Angus	279 days
Friesian	280 days
Hereford	282 days
Ayrshire	284 days
Charolais	285 days
Limousin	287 days
Guernsey	287 days

To achieve a calving interval of 365 days, the cow needs to become pregnant about twelve weeks after her previous calving date. Of course, she is unlikely to come into oestrus conveniently on the eighty-fifth day. Do not be tempted even to try and get a cow into calf for *at least* sixty days after calving: all cows need a really good rest before becoming pregnant again.

Cows are not seasonal breeders like so many other herbivores: they can come into heat at any time of year. The timing of the cow's oestrus cycle does not seem to depend on daylength, for example, though such factors can affect the *length* of the oestral period. (In winter, heats tend to be much shorter and it is therefore more difficult to catch the right moment for insemination.) The date of the first oestrus after calving can range from a few days to several weeks and the wild, feral or suckling cow tends to delay her first heat until the calf is well enough grown not to rely so heavily on her milk. The delay generally lasts for about three months and, since the pregnancy is a nine-month one and since the wild cow is likely to conceive during her first heat, she does effectively set up a natural pattern of calving once every twelve months, which is to say that the *individual* cow does breed 'seasonally'. Even in the dairy herd, some cows seem to adjust their heat periods to that they eventually calve almost on the same date every year.

Whatever the size of the herd, from one housecow to several hundred head of dairy cows, every excuse should be found for simply standing and staring at the cows. If you know what their 'normal' behaviour patterns are, you will soon notice anything out of the ordinary, whether it is a bulling cow or a sick one. What will you be looking for? With a housecow on her own, some people claim it is very difficult to know when she is bulling but in fact, if you know your cow at all, you will soon realise that she is more restless than usual, that her milk yield is perhaps lower for a day or two, that she is shouting a bit – often pacing the boundaries and calling out for no particular reason other than to broadcast her oestrus to any bull who might happen to be within earshot. If you know her really well, you might be able to identify a change of tone in her voice too, from a major to a minor key, and you might find that she is more than usually affectionate towards you or possibly even attempts to mount you. There may be signs of a clear mucous discharge from a slightly swollen vulva, smeared across her rump by her tail, and her tail-head might be slightly raised.

It is easier to spot bulling if there is more than one animal. Watch out for general restlessness and more aggressive social encounters than usual – a cow will engage in locking heads with other cows, for example. As she approaches her heat, she becomes a general nuisance making lying cows get up, resting her chin on other cows or grooming them more attentively than usual, and soon she tries to mount them, even over the head rather than rump. When other cows mount her rump, she stands still and this is *the* identifying factor of a bulling cow in 'standing oestrus'. Non-bulling cows will mount but will *not* stand to be mounted. Some cows are less 'attractive' than others and may be mounted so infrequently that you miss seeing them. This is particularly the case with more dominant cows.

Finally, nearly all heifers and perhaps 50% of cows show traces of a slightly bloody discharge (the 'bulling string') two days after oestrus, whether or not they have conceived.

When you have observed the first oestrus after calving, *make a note of the date*. Look out for a repeat of the behaviour about three weeks later and, again, record the date. If you missed the other signs, record the date of the one-day tell-tale bulling string. The pattern of her cycle will soon emerge and you will be ready to take the necessary steps to get her into calf at the right time. After insemination keep an eye out for her next scheduled oestrus to check whether or not she returns to service.

There are a few aids to heat detection if observation proves inadequate or difficult. Some farmers train 'sniffer' dogs to identify bulling cows; some use special patches that change colour, or tail-paste which gets rubbed off by mounting cows. A vasectomised bull can be fitted with a marker pad (the vasectomy renders him incapable of fertilising the cow's egg though he is still fully capable of going through all the motions). There are laboratory methods, such as measuring the progesterone levels in the cow's milk (they fall just before oestrus) or keeping a check on the temperature of the milk (a rise of at least $0.1°C$ above any temperature for the previous fifteen days) or recording the electrical resistance of vaginal mucus (levels are lowest at oestrus) or, more simply, noting a drop in milk yield which might be as much as 12–16% on the day before standing oestrus (lactation curves often show a definite downward kink every three weeks at this time).

There are also various hormone treatments which induce cows or heifers to come on heat to order. The treatment does not affect the cow's fertility: nutrition is far more influential on her chance of pregnancy.

CONDITION AT SERVICE

The cow's body condition at the time of service is important. If she is expected to calve to a 365-day interval or thereabouts, she will be served at a time when she is still producing a very high milk yield and she will inevitably have lost weight and condition after calving. It is common for cows in the early stages of their lactation to have an energy deficit: their appetites are lower than usual, so that they eat less and thus their energy intake is decreased, but as their milk output is increasing they make up the energy deficit by using body reserves, particularly by converting fat stores. The adequacy of those reserves depends on the nutrition levels of the period before calving, and it takes some time for the appetite to build up again after calving. The post-calving period is inevitably a time of stress, too: the cow may have been deprived of her calf, and a first-calver is adjusting to a new lifestyle and finding her social level in the group.

Body condition scoring is explained in the appendix. Any weight changes can be estimated by weighing the cow or, more easily, by measuring her heart-girth with a specially calibrated tape. Feeding levels should be aimed at limiting her weight loss in early lactation but her actual condition at the time of service is probably less important than the rate of change in the condition. She should be on a maintained or gradually rising plane of condition at service to increase her fertility, but a high-yielding cow simply will not have the appetite to eat as much as she needs to increase bodyweight as well as synthesise milk. (See fig. xiv overleaf.)

INFERTILITY

The most likely cause of apparent infertility is your failure to observe the cow's oestrus. Other common causes are nutritional, especially inadequate proteins, minerals and vitamins or an excess of fat. Copper, iodine and the vitamins A and D are especially important. Certain abnormalities or diseases can also affect fertility – for example cystic ovaries, retention of corpus luteum, post-calving infections and venereal disease.

A heifer who fails to conceive after, say, three inseminations might be an undetected freemartin, i.e. the twin of a bull calf. Twins are quite rare in cattle and if they are one of either sex there tends to be a transfer of hormones in the womb which result in the heifer being infertile. The male twin may have been aborted or reabsorbed very early in the pregnancy so that no one even knew it existed.

Cows for the Smallholder

Fig. xiv RECOMMENDED CONDITION SCORES

AT SERVICE:	Suckler cow	2.5
	Dairy cow	2.5
	Heifer	2.5–3.5
AT CALVING:	Suckler cow (spring calving)	2.5
	Suckler cow (autumn calving)	3.0
	Dairy cow	3.0–3.5
	[Mean milk yield highest if she calves at 3.5]	
WEIGHT CHANGES:	In early lactation there is a drop in liveweight of about 30kg, representing a loss of 1 condition score. (In heifers, 15kg represents a loss of 1 score.) At grass an increase of 60kg in cows (90kg in heifers) corresponds to an increase of 1 condition score (pregnancy complicates it!).	

BULL OR AI?

Once upon a time, you would have wandered your bulling cow down the lane to the nearest bull and left the pair to get on with it, or perhaps you would have discreetly allowed her to escape and find her own partner. It is a little different now and you can choose one of at least three methods of getting a cow into calf.

The natural way is the easiest if you have access to a bull, and it is certainly much the simplest if you have a group of heifers. Dairy farms tend to leave a bull running with the heifers once they are big enough to be mated; you can be fairly sure the bull (if he is of proven fertility) will serve every animal as soon as her time comes and the only problem is that you may not know the exact date of service for each heifer so you cannot calculate the due date of calving. A free-running bull might serve the same female anything up to ten times in one heat period and conception rates are very high indeed. If the heifers are still young enough to be growing, use a small-framed beef breed of bull (perhaps an Aberdeen Angus or a Hereford) to avoid potential calving problems in the young mothers.

If you keep your own bull in a yard and pen, he will help with identifying bulling cows. Make sure they all pass his yard regularly on their way to milking or feeding. The bullers will pay him attention whereas the rest pass by with hardly a glance in his direction, and his very presence may be enough to encourage 'silent heat' cows to be more demonstrative.

There is a very slightly higher rate of conception for cows served by a bull rather than given artificial insemination – about 71% of cows hold to first service by bull, compared to 68% with AI – as long as the bull is fertile. Don't blame the cow for the bull's lack of vigour! There are personal preferences, too: some cows will never hold to AI but will readily conceive by a familiar bull, especially if he is allowed a proper courtship period. Even when a cow is in 'standing' oestrus, she requires a few civil preliminaries on his part and needs to be reassured that his intentions are, if not honourable, then at least non-aggressive, so that her natural escape responses are allayed.

Artificial insemination gives you a very wide choice of proven, high-quality donor bulls and there are plenty of records on which to base your choice of sire. An insemination costs only a few pounds: all you have to do is observe the oestrus, lift the telephone and dial your local AI centre. If you call very early in the morning, the inseminator can be on the cowshed doorstep within hours. Your job is to have the cow waiting peacefully and adequately restricted for what is quite a skilled procedure. The inseminator has a margin of error of less than a centimetre and needs to concentrate on the work without having to worry about a dancing cow. It helps if the area is familiar to the cow and she should have adequate water and some food to keep her occupied while she waits, and preferably another cow to keep her company. A relaxed cow is much more likely to 'take' to the insemination.

Only licensed AI centres may collect bull semen for processing and distribution, and then only from bulls approved for the purpose by the Ministry. If you want to store bull semen for use on the farm, you must apply for a Ministry licence, which will specify the AI centre through which you should obtain the semen. (You can get the address of your nearest AI centre from the Ministry's divisional office – whether MAFF, MMB or a commercial breeding group.) Imported semen must be licensed; indeed you should talk to the Animal Health Department at Surbiton about importing anything to do with your herd, be it live animals, semen or embryos.

In the fast-developing world of genetics, you are no longer restricted to bulls and AI, and embryo transplant is one of the newer techniques. By this method a prize donor cow can be persuaded to superovulate and release a series of eggs, which are extracted from her and fertilised *in vitro*. The resultant embryos may even be split in half to create identical twins, and the sex of each embryo can be determined. They are then transplanted into the wombs of lesser cows, perhaps chosen for their ability to calve easily, who act rather like surrogate mothers, 'rent-a-womb' cows. They might each be given a single embryo, or might be asked to harbour twins from a split embryo. An embryo can be frozen for future use or transferred straight to the waiting receptor cow by means of surgical implantation or by a simple technique similar to AI.

Thus the prize cow can generate lots of prize calves quickly instead of just one calf a year. The technologists are excited. They are now talking about collecting stimulated ovaries from slaughtered cows and removing the eggs for *in vitro* fertilisation, or inseminating superovulated cows immediately before slaughter and then stealing the fertilised eggs from the dead mother's uterus. Sexed eggs of specific breeding can be put on the shopping-list along with AI straws. Twinning techniques could go further – triplets, quads . . . No doubt the day will come when cows, who are, after all, born with three teats too many for their usual single calf, will have multiple calvings and begin to think in terms of litters, like pigs and dogs. Isn't science wonderful? Ethically speaking – well, that is for you to decide.

Which bull?
There are those who, Ford-like, will use any bull so long as he is fertile, and there are those who are specialist breeders and enjoy the challenge of selecting exactly the right bull for exactly the right cow, either to produce top-class purebred calves or to experiment with crossbreeding programmes. If you have the skill, the time (present and future) and the money, the art of breeding is an addictive and intriguing one to which you can easily devote your entire life, and that of your heirs and successors. It is a particularly valuable art when your interest is in rare breeds, in which case you owe it to the breed to learn a lot more about genetics. Inbreeding is a natural hazard for low-number breeds and the results can be disastrous. If you do keep rare breeds, consult the Rare Breeds Survival Trust.

The majority of cow-keepers will strike a happy medium between the Ford approach and that of the specialist breeder. If your cows are registered pedigree dairy animals, you need to choose whether to go for a bull of the same breed so that you can register the calf with the breed society or whether to go for a beef bull to give you a more saleable calf on the beef market to help your cashflow. If you can guarantee that your Jersey cow will always produce heifer calves, choose a well-proven Jersey bull and build up a small milking herd to be proud of. But it does not work like that and you will no doubt have a run of Jersey bull calves, which might be good for your home freezer one day but for which no butcher will give you tuppence.

If you have a less than purebred cow, you may want to 'grade up' your herd so that eventually your stock can be registered with a breed society. This is achieved by using purebred bulls on the cows and on the successive generations until the proportion of purebred blood is sufficiently high to make them acceptable. Check with the breed society: each has its own rules for grading up.

As for the actual bull to use once the breed is chosen, and which cow is suitable for which bull, bear in mind that some characteristics are more readily inherited than others. The degree of heritability varies from breed to breed and a detailed analysis is inappropriate here, but the table below gives a very general idea of what you can most easily improve if you are breeding your own line or type of animal.

Fig. xv HERITABILITY

High	*Medium*	*Low*
% Solids-not-fat	Milk yield	Temperament
Height	Milking speed	Susceptibilty to mastitis
% Butterfat		Length of productive
% Protein		life
Weight		
Food conversion rates		

THE PREGNANT COW

The first question must be: 'Is she in calf?' The fact that a cow is or is not observed to be bulling again at the expected time of her next heat after insemination does not indicate categorically whether or not she is pregnant.

For a start, the insemination may indeed have been successful but about a quarter of fertilised eggs die in the first three weeks, and a further 5–10% die within the fourth to sixth weeks, and a few more even after that. And in about 5% of cases, a cow can show signs of oestrus even though she is in fact pregnant.

There are several methods of pregnancy diagnosis. The most common is manual palpation through the cow's rectum by the vet, who will not be able to make much sense of what he can feel until a heifer is at least six weeks pregnant and a cow perhaps ten or twelve weeks. Then the results are accurate and instant and the vet can probably carry out any necessary treatment on the spot.

The earliest diagnosis is by the MMB's milk progesterone test twenty-two to twenty-six days after service, but the results can sometimes be misleading. The same criticism can be levelled at ultrasonic detection, which needs expensive equipment to monitor foetal heartbeats and which cannot be used reliably until six to eight weeks into the pregnancy. An oestrone sulphate test on the milk is much cheaper and is very accurate but is of no value until fifteen weeks after service. But techniques for pregnancy diagnosis are being improved all the time and it is worth talking to your vet about them.

The first three weeks of pregnancy are crucial to the future of the new embryo and you should take some care to ensure that the cow is not put under stress either in handling, or by mixing her with a new social group, or putting her in a strange environment, or by suddenly changing her routines or rations.

Cow feeding is closely linked to milk yield and to the cow's breeding cycle, both in quantity and quality, and it is time to take a look at some of the factors which need to be taken into account in deciding on a breeding cow's rations. The way she is fed now will have an effect on the growth and health of the foetus as well as on her output of milk to the bucket, the machine or the suckling calf.

THE LACTATION CURVE

Every cow should have one! That is, every cow's output of milk should be recorded and charted unless it is going straight from the teat into a calf. Even then it is useful to have some idea of the cow's normal milk yield and pattern so that the calf's feeding can be adjusted accordingly.

If you are milking a housecow you are in an ideal position to learn about lactation curves in general and your own cow's in particular. Those who manage large dairy herds would do well to start at housecow level so that they can really understand cows as individuals.

Those who are willing and able to record daily yields will benefit from being immediately aware of the cow's moods and state of health. Lactations generally follow quite a smooth pattern, and any hiccups could well highlight an undetected oestrus, a fault in milking techniques and equipment, or the first stages of a health problem. All farmers, major or minor, should draw a few lactation curves just to see what is happening and where they might be going wrong. A graph is a picture, and a picture is much easier to understand at a glance than columns of figures or strings of words. (See fig. xvi.)

You will notice immediately that the daily yield climbs rapidly to a peak coinciding with the growing demands of the calf and then gradually declines as the calf becomes less dependent on the cow. The curve is similar whether or not she is suckling a calf – nature knows not the difference between a calf and a milking machine or human hands.

The timing and scale of the peak and the decreasing slope of the curve vary according to breed, management and the individuality of the cow. In general, peak yields are achieved at perhaps three to six weeks after calving, and the peak level is maintained for perhaps a couple of weeks before it begins to decline at an average rate of about 2.5% a week. Heifers reach a lesser peak and decline more gradually. The daily yield at the peak is generally about 0.5% of the total yield over the current lactation (about 0.45% for heifers) based on a standard lactation length of 305 days. So if your housecow gives a peak yield of, say, 20kg a day, her total yield during the whole lactation will be about 4,000kg (or, if you think imperial, a

Fig. xvi THE LACTATION CURVE

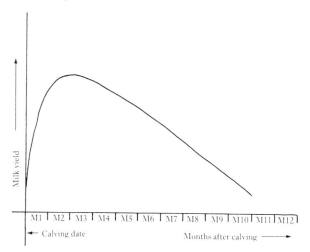

4 gallon peak will prophesy a total yield of about 800 gallons over the lactation). Thus the higher the peak, the higher the total for each lactation. You should adjust the cow's production ration to take account of her milk yield. Autumn calvers, incidentally, tend to give more milk than spring calvers because their yield is boosted by grass at spring turnout and remains higher for the lactation.

DRYING OFF

In a well-managed dairy herd with a calving index of about 365 days, the cow is deliberately dried off a couple of months before calving again to give her a break from milking. The process of drying off is quite simple: the yield will often be quite low at this stage and basically you just stop milking the cow. Leave her udder well alone and after a day or two she reabsorbs the milk and becomes dry. If her yield is still reasonable, dry her off more gradually by milking once a day for a few days and cutting out any concentrate feeding. Take sensible precautions against the entry of infections into the teats by using a long-lasting intramammary antibiotic – the so-called 'dry cow treatment'.

STEAMING UP

Commercial dairy farmers aim to maximise that peak yield and they anticipate milk production requirements by feeding the cow appropriately some time before she actually calves, at the period when the foetus is growing very fast a month or so before it is born. This pre-calving period coincides with the cow's dry period and the aim is not only to feed the growing foetus (indirectly) but also to build up the cow's body reserves so that she is on a rising plane of nutrition when she calves. It also prepares her long-suffering stomachs for the large quantities of concentrates which many farmers believe are essential in the early stages of lactation to boost yields to a maximum peak. It is possible to increase total potential milk yields by more than 10% if you feed the pre-calver in such a way that she is gaining up to half a kilogram of bodyweight per day, and this pumping-up process in the pre-calving period is known as 'steaming up'.

Steaming-up rations usually begin gradually four to six weeks before calving. The cow will have been dry for at least a couple of weeks, then concentrates are introduced again little by little until she is being fed about a half or threequarters of the amount you expect to feed her at peak yield. Make sure she is also getting an adequate supply of good-quality fodder and base your concentrate calculations on the quality of that food. Bear in mind that the greatly expanded uterus of the pregnant cow can restrict the capacity of the rumen.

Do not oversteam a heifer: give her a maximum of 3kg of concentrates a day unless she is in such poor condition that she really needs building up. Be very wary of over-conditioning a pregnant animal: if she is too fat at calving she will have all sorts of problems both during and after parturition. Be especially wary of oversteaming dual-purpose cows like the Dexter or breeds like the Shetland and Kerry which are used to roughing it and are just not designed for intensive management. In fact, unless you are determined to extract high yields, think very carefully about whether steaming up is desirable at all, whatever the breed.

Some people demand far too much of the cow and one disguised blessing of the quota system is that some farmers realise it is better to demand less of the individual cow and to adjust her rations by reducing expensive concentrates in favour of a greater proportion of cheaper bulk food of good quality. But a proper balance must be struck: concentrates can be a vital source of minerals and vitamins which might be lacking in forage.

CALVING

It is sound practice to fetch in pregnant heifers and cows daily for at least the month before calving. It will give you a good opportunity for closer examination; it will also get a skittish heifer used to being restricted and handled, and she will be much quieter when the time comes to begin milking her. (She is referred to as a heifer until she bears her first calf: thereafter she becomes a cow or, to some people, a first-calf heifer with no right to call herself a cow until she has had a second calf.)

Fig. xvii THE YEAR OF THE COW

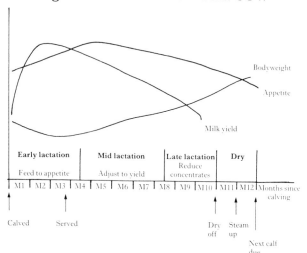

Early lactation	Mid lactation	Late lactation	Dry
Feed to appetite	Adjust to yield	Reduce concentrates	

Bodyweight

Appetite

Milk yield

M1 M2 M3 M4 M5 M6 M7 M8 M9 M10 M11 M12 Months since calving

Calved   Served   Dry off   Steam up

Next calf due

Check udders for any signs of discomfort or peculiar swellings. The udder usually begins to 'bag up' three or four days before calving: the previously soft, deflated bag fills with milk and can become quite plump and tight. It is a useful warning sign that calving is fairly imminent; some heifers bag up more than a week before calving and some cows leave it until the last moment, only bagging up for a day or so. On the whole it is best to leave the udder alone unless the cow seems unduly concerned and uncomfortable. If your fingertips leave no depression when you press them against the sole of the udder, and it feels hard and hot and is clearly painful, you can release some of the pressure by milking out a little from each quarter – just enough to ease the discomfort. Once you have done so, you must continue at intervals because the very act of milking will stimulate a further build-up of pressure. The cow might appreciate a gentle massage of her udder, with no milk being extracted, and this would be preferable. Otherwise leave it alone. The cow's first milk is something very precious for the well-being of the newborn calf and should not be wasted.

Most cows, especially typical suckler breeds, are happier and healthier choosing their own nursery in the field, and if the place is free of infection, reasonably dry underfoot, has sheltered areas for privacy and no hazards like open ditches, let her do as she pleases. But if any problems are likely, neither you nor the vet will want to chase her all over the field on a dark, wet night. Incidentally, a calf born out in the field with full freedom can become almost impossible to catch in no time at all, should you need to do so.

If you intend to calve indoors, give her ample opportunity to become familiar with the calving quarters beforehand and bring her in finally a few days before the calf is due so that she really feels at home. If you take her in too suddenly, she will probably clap her legs together and delay the whole business for a day or two.

The loosebox should be very clean indeed, thoroughly scrubbed out and disinfected in advance, and well bedded with straw. Make sure she has plenty of space but do not just shut her in all the time. She needs adequate exercise to be fit for calving and also to avoid constipation. If anything, her dung should be a little on the loose side and if necessary you can give her a bran mash (scalded bran with molasses) but do not overdo it. A purgative at this stage could even cause her to abort. Go gently on her diet in these last few days: reduce the concentrates and the overall protein content of the ration a little to avoid an uncomfortably full udder.

If you know your cow, you will be very aware of the imminence of calving even if you failed to keep a careful diary note of the expected date. Many of the signs are hard to describe – it is more a case of understanding the cow and being in sympathy with her so that you recognise subtle changes in behaviour and mood. Some cows are very dreamy and affectionate a day or two before calving, for example. Others become increasingly restless and talkative. Most tend to withdraw from their group, looking for a private calving place, though some make little preparation and hardly seem to be aware of the coming event. Many cows become much meeker, turning aside from the slightly aggressive encounters that are part of the everyday social life of a cow.

The physical symptoms are clearer. Two or three days before calving, the vulva begins to look swollen, flabby and pink and there may be a slight discharge of clear mucus. The udder begins to bag up three or four days before her time, and her appetite drops quite noticeably a day or two later. Perhaps the most definitive symptom is that, as some farmers say, 'her pin bones drop'. This is not as noisy or uncomfortable as it sounds: it actually means that the pelvic ligaments (not bones) on either side of the tail-head slacken to allow the pelvic outlet to be stretched for the birth. You will be able to slip the edge of your hand, or even your fist, into the little hollows that will form between the tail-head and the pin bones – bones which in a Jersey are particularly obvious on either side of the tail-head.

Most cows calve quite easily and happily all on their own and this is often their preference – so much so that, like mares, they may be careful not to calve while you are present, however much they trust you, and will then drop the calf in the quick half-hour break you took for some sleep or a meal. More often than not you will find a clean, dry calf already at her udder with its tail wagging merrily when you go down at daybreak. On the other hand, a heifer having her first calf could well need help and might also gain reassurance from your presence. Some say that a heifer will only allow herself to be milked by a person who was present at the calving.

Although most calvings seem to take place in the hours of darkness, especially in the darkest ones before dawn, it is not usually necessary to sit up all night with a cow even if you anticipate difficulties with the calving. If you check her just before midnight, she will almost certainly defer calving until the morning. However, if the cow does have a history of problems, or if you have put her to a bull whose offspring tend to be very large, you should take no chances and should try to be present for the birth whenever it takes place. You will need another person standing by in case of difficulties: it often takes two people to help a cow in trouble. You should also forewarn your vet.

About three days before the birth the foetus makes its own preparations to move into position. A day before, it is nearly ready: forelegs pointing towards its exit, neck unbent and head stretched along the forelegs, and its body being slowly rotated to align for the birth. The little creature has been exercising itself in the womb for quite some time and its muscles are now ready for the work ahead. In the final hours, if it is healthy, it will be positioned as if about to take a running dive out of the womb. If it fails to be active during that final day, it will not have positioned itself and will be wrongly presented, so that the birth could be a difficult one.

The normal birth is in three stages: a preliminary period of discomfort with a gradual increase in straining at intervals while pacing about, then the serious and intense strainings of the actual birth and finally the passing of the afterbirth.

Preliminaries

The cow's restlessness increases as the hour draws near. She keeps fidgeting, changing her position, lying down and getting up again, behaving almost as if she had indigestion and perhaps kicking at her belly. She will be on the alert, eyes and ears checking the environment constantly. She is basically cheerful but there are obvious intermittent spasms of discomfort and she will strain for a few seconds every now and then. By the end of this stage the increasing frequency of the contractions may lead to the breaking of the first waterbag, which empties as a straw-coloured liquid looking very like urine.

The birth

The cow might take a breather for an hour or so before the second stage. Straining becomes far more powerful, each session lasting perhaps half a minute. She really begins to concentrate on the job and becomes quite oblivious to her surroundings. She is probably lying down by now, either in a normal resting position or flat on her side. After several straining bouts the tips of the calf's feet appear, then its tongue, followed after a while by its nose and head. Once its chest and half its trunk are out, she may well get to her feet and complete the delivery standing up so that the calf's hindquarters slip out quite quickly and the umbilical cord breaks as the little one drops safely to the ground.

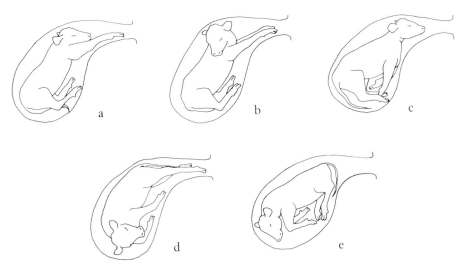

Calf presentations in the uterus at the time of birth:
(a) Normal presentation: forefeet emerging first, followed by muzzle
Wrong presentations:
(b) Forefeet first but head turned back
(c) Muzzle first, forelegs tucked back
(d) Hindlegs first and upside down
(e) The breech: buttocks first

Afterbirth

The final stage is the passing of the afterbirth or placenta, usually within an hour or two but it can be several hours or even a couple of days. The cow will probably eat it: for one thing it is valuable protein, and for another her instinct is to remove evidence of the birth in case there are any predators in the vicinity. The chapter on health explains what to do if the afterbirth is retained.

Helping

Do not interfere with the birth unless it is essential to do so. Indeed, the more a cow is inspected or handled during calving, the more likely she is to have problems. Give her *time* and do not be too eager to use a rope and help the calf on its way. If it is presented correctly – forefeet first, then nose –

leave the cow to get on with it, in complete privacy, for a few hours. If there is still no progress at all eight hours later, call the vet. But if the nose and tongue are already protruding and nothing more has happened after a couple of hours, the tongue and head will swell and help will be needed to ease the head out into the open by carefully looping the calving rope (scrupulously clean) over the top of the calf's head and behind its ears and then pulling and releasing in time with the cow's own efforts. If the calf is stuck at the hips, it is best to call the vet unless you are experienced.

If during the second stage the cow has been straining *intensely* for perhaps two hours (four if she is a heifer) with nothing to show for it, there may be a malpresentation and you will need the vet.

If the feet come out upside down, with the soles showing uppermost, they might be hind feet rather than forefeet or the calf itself might be upside down. Other malpresentations include the head being turned right back, or one or both forelegs turned back, or the calf lying with nose and chin tucked down instead of stretching forwards, or (most common of all) the breech presentation with the calf coming out backwards and the hind legs in a variety of positions. Do not be tempted to jeopardise the life of the calf and possibly the cow by fiddling around trying to help when you do not know enough about it: you could very easily cause a greater disaster by interfering. Seek experienced assistance.

Once the calf has been born, a heifer might panic at this strange, alien object she has produced; she might ignore it completely or might even threaten it. An exhausted or sick cow after a difficult calving might be unable or unwilling to attend to her calf, and then it is up to you. If the membranes are not cleared from the calf's nostrils, it will not be able to breathe, and a calf worn out by a difficult birth very easily gives up. Wipe away the membranes with a wisp of clean straw then tickle a straw up its nostrils to help it take its first breath. If the calf is too weak to respond, you can give it the kiss of life or artificial respiration, or you can hold the calf upside down and chuck a bucket of cold water over its head and chest.

THE NEW MOTHER AND HER CALF

An experienced cow will know all about the urgent cleaning up of her new calf and will lick it vigorously. The maternal bond is established within the first few minutes – a crucial period. Thereafter the cow will be deeply disturbed if the calf is taken away from her, and in many cases she is most unlikely to accept a foster once her natural bonding with her own calf has been formed.

All that early licking after the birth helps to create the bond and makes the smell of the calf familiar to the cow, and the calf's first wobbling attempts at rising after the birth trigger off all sorts of maternal instincts.

You will hear the cow's special calf-talk, too, as she teaches the calf just who *she* is.

The new calf explores its new world more by touch than anything else. Its eyesight is limited at first and it leads with its nose, holding its head about level with the rest of its body. Usually it bumps into its mother who, if she is experienced, will stand still while it explores her body in its own time; she won't fidget when it latches on to anything it can find at approximately the right height above ground and she will discreetly position herself so that it follows her abdominal curves towards the udder. The calf is attracted to the shade of her underbelly and it noses its way along her contours until it touches the unique texture of her udder. Now it seeks something protruding: the shape of a teat is the next tactile landmark and once it has found a teat (in the majority of cases it will be a front one) and taken a few tentative sucks it quickly learns what a rewarding activity teat-sucking can be. Quite often it is suckling within an hour of birth but it may take longer to locate the teats on a rather pendulous udder or with a less co-operative cow or a startled heifer. In the meantime it will attempt to suck anything it can get hold of until it discovers that a tuft of elbow hair or hock is not in the least fruitful.

This first meal is vital and it is most important that the calf suckles within its first five or six hours of life. If you are not present at the time, you can tell that the calf has suckled when it passes black, jelly-like droppings, stimulated by its mother's thorough washing of its bottom whilst it suckles (just like a bitch with her pups). If it seems to have trouble in getting the milk flow going, help by massaging the cow's udder and milking out the first few drops. Once the calf tastes the milk, it will be well away in no time.

Colostrum

That early meal gives the calf its first fill of colostrum, a magic substance which gives it antibodies against infections in its immediate environment. Without that protection it is doomed. If the calf fails to feed properly in its first six hours of life it never will achieve adequate immunity. It needs about a pint of colostrum to avoid death from blood poisoning and another six to avoid diarrhoea; and if it manages to suck vigorously for about twenty minutes it should take in enough colostrum to survive.

If a cow is for some reason unable to suckle her calf and you have to hand-feed the colostrum from a bottle, it will absorb more if you feed it in its mother's presence than in isolation. If a cow dies in labour but her calf survives, it needs colostrum immediately and you should keep a stock of it in the freezer for such emergencies. The best protection is its own mother's colostrum but another cow's will give some measure of defence and in a real emergency you can use goat's milk colostrum – it will help, but maybe not enough.

The newly calved cow produces colostrum for the first four days of her lactation. It is a thick, sticky, yellow milk and you should let the calf have as much as it can take. Do not milk her yourself for the first day or two unless she really is bursting, and even then do not milk her right out. (Take a little for yourself if she can spare it: it sets like egg custard with no help from any added ingredients. The 'beestings', as this first milk used to be called, were always considered a delicacy.)

Colostrum contains more than antibodies. It is about 40% more nutritious than milk and is highly digestible; it is laxative and as long as the cow has been fed on good fodder it will be rich in carotene, which is the precursor of vitamin A. (The quality of colostrum is influenced by the cow's diet and state of health and it can deteriorate if the cow's dry period is less than four weeks or if she is ill during that period.) Any emergency colostrum substitute should meet as many of these qualities as possible, and the best compromise is a fresh egg beaten into a litre of warm milk and water (three parts milk to one part water) with a teaspoonful of cod liver oil, plus a dessertspoonful of castor oil as a laxative to encourage the passing of the foetal dung. You can feed this mixture three times a day for four days, giving a litre a time and omitting the castor oil once the foetal dung has been passed.

Fig. xviii COLOSTRUM AND MILK

COMPONENT		COLOSTRUM	MILK
Fat	(%)	3.6	3.5
Solids-not-fat	(%)	18.5	8.6
Protein	(%)	14.3	3.25
Immune globulin	(%)	6.0	0.09
Calcium	(%)	0.26	0.13
Carotenoids	(g/g fat)	25–45	7
Vitamin A	(g/g fat)	42–48	8
Vitamin D	(ng/g fat)	23–45	15
Vitamin E	(g/g fat)	100–150	20
Vitamin B12	(g/g fat)	10–50	5

The calf's residual umbilical cord will probably be about 20cm long and it is often a point of entry for infection. Dip it in iodine as a precaution, or spray with chloromycetin or dress with sulphanilamide powder. The cord will shrivel and drop off of its own accord within a week or so of the birth.

The cow, too, is at some risk for the first few days. The most immediate problem might be milk fever, uterine prolapse or retention of afterbirth, and the symptoms and treatments of these and other problems (including abortion) are covered in Chapter 8.

Now comes the moment of truth and trauma. Will she be allowed to keep her calf and suckle it as she would wish for a few months? Or will she be asked to share its milk either with you or with foster calves? Or will you demand all her milk and deprive her of her calf entirely? That, of course, depends upon your enterprise and conscience. A commercial dairy farmer will not hesitate for a moment: the calf will either be removed within minutes of birth and given its colostrum by bottle, or it will be left with its mother for four days until her milk becomes saleable and the demands of the bulk tank weigh more heavily than those of the calf or the cow's maternal bond. The longer they are left together, the more traumatic will be the parting. Take the calf away from the cow (never vice versa) and keep the mother out of earshot of her bawling offspring, and equally keep her calf out of earshot of its bellowing mother, who will shout her head off for at least two days and nights. She will settle down eventually and resign herself to being milked, and her calf too will eventually come to terms with its new situation.

It does seem unfair, doesn't it? But, then, the domestication of animals has always been for their exploitation by human beings. You can work out your own compromises if you believe that animals are rather more than insensitive machines whose role in life is to serve our needs.

VII

CALVES

Out in the wild, a newborn calf suckles perhaps every five hours during its first day or two and increases the rate to perhaps every three hours or so over the next few days. Ten-minute suckles usually fulfil its needs and it spends much of the rest of the day sleeping and resting. By the time it is six months old, it is probably suckling three or four times a day.

At birth, the calf can only obtain its sustenance from milk. Its abomasum is at least three times the size of the rumen and it is not physically capable of making use of roughage or solid foods. When it suckles, its head is raised to the udder and the milk is channelled direct to the abomasum by a special oesophageal groove, bypassing the other stomachs. Because it drinks little and often, each feed forms small clots in the abomasum and the digestive juices have plenty of surface area to work on.

Within the first week or two, a calf will begin to play with a few wisps of grass or hay. At first this is just a gesture and trial but it begins to nibble and swallow some of the fodder, which goes into its rumen and encourages that all-important stomach to develop and grow, little by little, as the intake of fibre gradually increases. By the time the calf is eight weeks old, the rumen is at least three times as big as the abomasum: proportions have been reversed and solid food is increasingly important and effectively digested.

If calves are to be reared artificially, without the benefit of their mothers' udders, those natural suckling patterns and stomach developments must be taken into account and should form the basis of whatever system you choose.

There are several options open to calf-rearers:
* Single suckling (calf on its own mother)
* Foster suckling (calf on a nurse cow)
* Double suckling (two calves on one cow together)
* Multiple suckling (one cow suckling successive batches of calves – up to twelve in one lactation)
* Artificial suckling (bottle, or calf feeders with teats)
* Artificial bucket-rearing (milk drunk, not sucked)

With artificial rearing you can opt for natural milk or milk substitutes and replacers, fed warm or cold, and available once, twice or three times a day or on the *ad lib* 'cafeteria' system. You can choose between early weaning (no more milk after five weeks) or late weaning (e.g. suckling the cow for six months). You can rear home-born calves or buy some in when convenient, or go in for contract-rearing of dairy replacement calves. Whichever the system, the calves are generally healthier if you copy nature as far as possible: feed little and often, at blood temperature (or if it is cold, feed little and often so it has a chance to warm up easily in the stomach), provide initial privacy but thereafter keep calves in established groups all the same size and age, and give free access to best hay and fresh water from an early age to develop the rumen. You should also observe very strict hygiene indeed with all housing and equipment (including your own hands) and should always treat calves of any age with kind firmness, patience and understanding.

SUCKLING

Suckled calves generally develop more quickly and are more robust than artificially reared calves, whichever system you choose. Dairy cows can be used but they have been specifically bred for high milk yields and will give far too much for a single calf. The milk of Channel Island breeds may be too rich for a calf, especially a foster, which could find it indigestible or might develop an allergy that takes all the hair off its face.

Non-dairy breeds are better designed as sucklers, especially the hardy hill cows who typically run free and drop their calves out of doors with great ease, asking no help from anyone. Suckler cows are usually managed so that the whole group calves round about the same time, in spring or in autumn, and they know their job very well. They rarely need assistance, and indeed often resent it. You should interfere with them as little as possible, especially at calving, because the essence of a successful suckler is the strong maternal bond that she forms with her calf.

Suckler cows usually calve down in quite thin condition. They rarely receive concentrates and their hay ration can be bulked up with good feeding straw. They are generally much healthier than dairy cows, partly because of their breeding and partly because of their way of life, though they may have problems if you house them.

Spring-calving suckler systems work well and are economical: the grass grows with the calf and the calf will be a big one by October, when you can wean it, bring it in and start fattening. The basic aim of suckling is to let the cow buffer the calf, and some people carry that to the extreme by letting the calf grow splendidly at the expense of the cow's body reserves. That is hardly fair to the cow.

Calves should have access to creep feeding, i.e. a place where they can eat extra food in peace with the cows excluded. In the field, all you need is a few barriers across a corner to keep cows out but let calves in, with a weatherproof feeding trough. Loose-housed suckler calves need more supplementary feeding than those on grass and their creep area should give them extra comfort as well as food. As long as mother and calf remain easily visible to each other, they will be quite happy. Use rolling bars for easy calf access to an indoor creep and build in a means of holding the calves in the creep so that they can be handled for disbudding etc.

Creep feeding can be *ad lib* but take care that each calf is adequately fed and that the bullies don't grab the lot. They will probably be decidedly interested in hay by the time they are three weeks old and will also show some interest in concentrates, whether pelleted or in the form of home-mixed rations of crushed barley and flaked maize with soya-bean meal, beet pulp and fishmeal. Weaning is usually at about six months but depends on condition, season and markets.

Single suckling and milking

If you have a milch cow and want her to raise her own calf but do not want to put a second calf on her, you need to help yourself to some of her milk – it will be far too much for one calf, whatever its age, and it will start scouring. A four-day-old calf needs about one weight-unit of milk (fresh from the udder, or reconstituted from milk powder) for every ten units of its live bodyweight (a litre is equivalent to a kilogram, and a gallon to 10 lbs). Thus a typical Jersey calf would need about 5 pints or 3 litres a day, a Dexter perhaps 6 pints or 3.5 litres and a Friesian a gallon or 4.5 litres. That rate holds good up to about three weeks old.

You will find it much simpler to keep the calf out of udder-reach except at definite access times. You could, for example, house the calf and bring the cow into its loosebox at milking time but that is a pretty lonely life for a calf unless there are others around as well. Or you could house the calf in the cow's field so that they can share each other's company but the suckling is controlled: make a field shelter for the calf with an open front partitioned up to calf height so that the cow can reach over and groom the calf but the calf cannot get at her udder. If the partition is made of palings or poles set closer together than the width of a calf's muzzle, it will be able to see what is going on in the field and be much more contented than if it is deprived of the view. Then, when the time is convenient to you, bring the cow to the shelter, milk her and let the calf suck. Most calves prefer suckling from a favourite side, so with a good-tempered cow the happiest arrangement may be for you to milk from your side while the calf suckles from the other. Let-down will be excellent: the cow will want to feed the calf and your own extractions will be tolerated.

Foster suckling, double-suckling and multi-suckling

If you value a cow's milk too highly to allow her calf its ration you can compromise by using a nurse cow – perhaps an older cow past her best. Let the calf have its four days of colostrum from its own mother, then transfer it to the nurse cow, who can probably take more than one calf at a time if required, depending on her yield and temperament. At a rough estimate, each calf will need a total of perhaps 450kg of milk during a twelve to sixteen week fostering period.

Some cows are so maternal they will let any and every calf tug at their teats, and if you have a nurse cow of that temperament you should be most grateful and treat her with great respect. If she has just calved, however, even such a paragon may be less than welcoming to alien calves and you will have to use a combination of patience, firmness and skulduggery to persuade her to accept her foster calf or calves.

You could tie her in a pen and physically restrain her while the foster suckles (hold her tail up if she kicks, but she will probably withhold her milk). If she has just calved, shut the foster in the corner of her pen with her own calf and release both for suckling at the same time, keeping the cow restricted until she finally accepts the second calf as her own. If the foster's smell can be disguised by rubbing its coat with the cow's own afterbirth, she might be more amenable, or use some other smell just to confuse her – perhaps a perfume.

There are other ruses. While she is suckling her own calf, sneak the foster in to suckle between her hind legs and teach it that this will be its safest approach. Or blindfold the cow: she will be much quieter if she cannot see. But, above all, only use a generous, amenable cow as a nurse. If she is not that way inclined, don't fight her – and never use some of the unpleasant diversionary tactics that are sometimes recommended. The harsher or angrier you are with her, the more determined she will be to withhold her milk and kick off any calf you try and force upon her. Wouldn't you do the same in her situation? Think cow: her job is to protect and raise her *own* calf and, unlike sheep, cows very rarely steal each other's calves. To a cow, her calf is an extension of herself, but someone else's is not.

With multiple suckling the usual practice is to give the cow fresh batches of calves every ten weeks: four calves for the first ten weeks of her lactation, then three different ones for ten weeks, followed by another three, and finally just two new calves for weeks thirty-one to forty. Then give the poor old thing a rest.

ARTIFICIAL REARING

Suckled calves do best, if you can spare the cow's milk and have the space for cows. Dairy farms tend to rear their calves artificially or sell them off, and many holdings run bought-in calf-rearing enterprises without a cow in sight.

Such calves are at an immediate disadvantage. They have experienced the trauma of being removed from their mothers; they may or may not have been allowed sufficient time with her to acquire antibodies through her colostrum and her very presence; they may well have had the additional and severe stress of the marketplace as well as being bundled into a transporter; they have probably been in contact with all sorts of alien bacteria against which their home-nurtured resistance is little defence; and finally they find themselves in unfamiliar surroundings, subjected to unfamiliar routines, and are expected to thrive on powdered milk which may not even be warmed. It says a lot for the innate toughness of calves that more of them do not promptly turn up their toes and die. Quite a few of them do.

If you do buy in calves, give them a better chance by avoiding the marketplace altogether: fetch them direct from the home farm, find out exactly what feed and routines they have been used to and follow those precedents as far as possible, making any changes very gradually. New-comers should be kept well away from other calves until you are sure they are healthy and not harbouring some infection. If you see signs of scouring (diarrhoea), discharges from eyes or nose or a generally dispirited look about a calf with a staring coat, you could have a problem on your hands and you do not want it to spread.

Do not buy a calf unless you are very sure that its home farm has been diligent in giving it colostrum. Don't move it from its home farm until it is at least seven days old and then, when it arrives, let it rest quietly for a while after the journey, in the privacy of its own sheltered pen, before you give it a sustaining feed of glucose dissolved in warm water (perhaps 50g glucose per litre of water). Do not give it milk substitute until the third feed and even then only give it at half strength. Increase the strength gradually over the next week or so. Feed at regular hours, preferably at least three times a day, which may be inconvenient for you but you have opted to take responsibility for the calf and should put its needs ahead of your own.

Milk substitutes are normally based on powdered skim-milk with added vitamins and minerals, and often a proportion of added fat to increase the product's energy value and digestibility. They need very careful mixing at the right temperature, and all equipment should be scrupulously clean and thoroughly sterilised *every* time it is used. Remember that the odds are already against the calf.

The naturally suckled calf drinks cow-warm milk by sucking at a teat with its face uplifted. The artificially reared calf should at least be lucky enough to have warm milk substitute sucked in a similar position from an 'artificial cow', even something as simple as a bucket with a teat fixed underneath. Such systems, closely copying nature, will help restore the odds in the calf's favour. There are several devices on the market for feeding more than one calf at a time on teats but you must ensure that each calf knows how to use it and that even the meekest can get its fair share. Make sure that each calf actually knows how to *suck* (sadly, a calf which has not been allowed to suckle in its first week of life will never be able to do so) and use warm feeds to help the calves accept a new feeding system, then gradually reduce the temperature over several feeds if you intend to feed cold.

Cold feeds are made from acid milk replacers which counteract the digestive upset of a cold feed by adjusting the acidity levels in the abomasum so that the enzymes can function efficiently. If the replacer can be sucked through a teat rather than gulped from a bucket, results should be good. Ideally the calf should be allowed to use a cafeteria system whereby it can help itself when it feels the need to suckle, so that it is as near as possible to the natural pattern of 'little and often'. Make sure there is always a fresh supply on tap.

Bucket-feeding, though convenient for the farmer, comes unnaturally to a calf and hence it can lead to all sorts of digestive and behavioural upsets. For a start, the calf has to learn to drink rather than suck, and it has to take its feed head-down rather than head up. It is also given its feed in some bulk, often only twice or even only once a day, and the feed tends to be cold or at least cool. The net result is that the milk is not all safely channelled straight into the abomasum (some finds its way to the underdeveloped rumen) and what does arrive in the abomasum may be too cold for the digestive system to function efficiently and also comes all in a rush so that it forms one big indigestible lump rather than lots of small curds. The result is scouring, the scourge of calf-raisers.

A calf has to be trained to drink from a bucket by someone who has infinite patience and sympathy. Back the calf into a corner of its pen. Put a bucketful of warm feed between your knees, and have a relaxing conversation with the calf to reassure it. Give it your fingers to suck and gradually lower your hand into the feed so that the calf is still sucking your fingers as its muzzle dips into the milk. Avoid getting milk straight up its nostrils. Carefully remove your fingers after a little while and, with luck, after two or three guided attempts like this, it will find itself drawing in milk from the bucket instead of from your fingers. Never let it drink too fast or too much and never lose your temper with it while it is learning this strange new technique. Make sure its muzzle is free of milky residues and quite dry before it is released or returned to a group, because if it is still wet it will still want to suck and will latch on to whatever comes to mouth, like another calf's ear or navel, or the bars of the pen or a piece of dirty baler twine.

This compulsive sucking can be quite a problem with bucket-fed calves, especially in a group bunched together in an over-crowded pen and probably bored. The habit, once established, can persist into adult life. (People used to blame hedgehogs for stealing cows' milk in the night: perhaps it was really emotionally retarded cows who had never grown up, like thumb-suckers.) There are ways of deterring suck-minded calves and perhaps the best is to make them *work* for their meal so that they do not gulp it all down in a rush and find themselves still in a feeding frame of mind at the mouth end, whatever their bellies might say about being replete. The sucking reflex, once it has been activated by the taste of milk, tends to continue for a certain length of time regardless of whether or not the calf is still ingesting. The longer it takes a calf to drink its ration, therefore, the better in every respect. The sucking urge will be satisfied, and the stomach will find it easier to cope with a slower rate of intake. Ten minutes a feed should be about right, with at least three feeds a day.

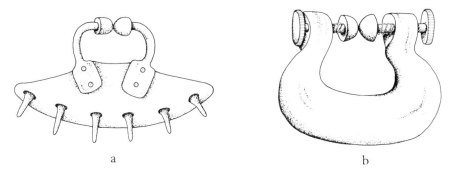

a   b

Nose-flap devices for deterring a heifer or cow from trying to suckle:
(a) Spiked plate encourages other cows to kick her away from their udders
(b) Hinged flap falls in front of the sucker's mouth as she raises her muzzle to the udder

If you are desperate about the problem, you can try deterrents like plastering dung on all the things a calf is likely to suck – which includes all the other calves' ears, navels and teats for a start! Or you can keep each calf separate after feeding, until it has dried its muzzle and lost the sucking urge.

Introduce dry foods at an early stage. They do not give as good weight gains as liquid diets but they do encourage development of the rumen, which is essential if you are on an early-weaning system. Top-quality hay (always save the best for the calves), fresh concentrates and ample fresh water should be available from the age of one week and the aim is to encourage the calves to be consuming 0.7–0.8kg of concentrates a day by the time they are weaned at five weeks old, or 0.9kg at six to eight weeks old. Bear in mind that young calves are designed to drink milk, which is closer to animal than vegetable, and they will do better if the concentrates contain some animal protein, like fishmeal.

If you are feeding milk replacers, you could give *ad lib* feeds to three weeks old and then start substituting cold water instead of milk replacer during the night. This will encourage the calves to eat dry foods, and you should put some very palatable high-protein concentrates (18% crude protein content) near the milk-feeding system to give them the right idea.

Whatever system you use, keep it simple and maintain a regular routine so that the calves know what to expect.

WEANING

Weaning, on any system, is generally an abrupt affair. As long as the calves are eating and easily digesting enough solid food, and are looking well and not scouring, you can simply stop the liquid feed all at once. Some people prefer the gradual process but that never works for cigarette addicts.

After weaning the calves should receive concentrates *ad lib*, up to a maximum of 2kg per calf per day, and the crude protein content can be reduced to 15–16%, with very good hay freely available. You could offer top-quality silage from six weeks old but they should still have hay as well. When they are about three months old they will be eating up to 2.7kg of concentrates a day and the protein content can be reduced to 14%, but hay and silage should still be available *ad lib*.

If the calves are autumn-born, their first grazing season will come when they are about six months old and they should be turned out on to your best grazing on pastures which have not been used by any other cattle for at least twelve months so that it is free of parasites. Young stock are very susceptible to worms and should be vaccinated against various parasites as a precaution before turn-out. Keep feeding some concentrates – perhaps one or two kilograms a day – until they are used to grass.

Spring-born calves will not be able to make best use of grass when they are early-weaned and should continue to receive good hay and 16% concentrates. As they are that much younger than autumn-born calves at turn-out, they are even more susceptible to pasture worms and it is essential that the grazing is clean.

Suckled calves do very well indeed on grass. The limitation of appetite for grass, which can hold back the growth of weaned spring calves, is no problem for a calf running with its mother, and sucklers also seem to gain some protection from worms by being with their dams, as long as the pasture is not too heavily stocked and infested. Well-managed grass supplemented with mother's milk is the best possible ration for a growing calf. The youngster also has the great benefit of being able to learn about life from its mother and the rest of the group – a benefit denied to the artificially reared calf who never sees any cattle other than its peers and they will not be able to teach it anything at all about selective grazing, or escaping from flies, or how to stand your ground in the face of a pompous cock pheasant. Somehow the suckled calf at pasture gets so much more from life: it plays more, it explores more, it learns more and it has *fun* – chasing butterflies, jumping back from stinging nettles, pestering all kinds of wildlife . . . Pity the artificially reared calf confined to its quarters without the stimulation of the big wide world outside.

ROUTINE MANAGEMENT

There are certain routines applicable to all calves, whatever their upbringing or ultimate fate.

Identification

The Ministry of Agriculture requires all stock to be identified permanently, before the animals are two weeks old, by markings in the right ear which include the Ministry's regional code, your holding code, and a number specific to the individual animal (usually a letter for the year of birth followed by a number 1 for the first calf born on the holding in that year, a 2 for the second and so on). The Ministry will give you details of approved methods of tagging or tattooing.

Your breed society will also demand a numbering system if the calf is to be registered. The society will allocate its own ear number and you can either use this instead of the Ministry number (as long as the Ministry knows about it) or perhaps put the number in the other ear.

Disbudding

For ease of later management, most horned breeds (especially of dairy cows) are deprived of their horns and the kindest time for such an operation is before the horns have actually grown. Calves of horned breeds are born with little knobs, or buds, from which their horns will develop. If you want a hornless animal you should 'disbud' the calf when it is two to three weeks old.

The kindest method is to use a cauterising iron heated by gas or electricity. For this you are legally required to ensure that the calf has a local anaesthetic and, unless you are competent to give such injections, it is best to ask the vet to do it for you. The needle must be placed with great accuracy at exactly the right point for each bud. It must of course be very sharp and very clean – I have seen calves with severe after-effects from dirty needles and it is not a pleasant sight.

How to hold a calf for disbudding. [Farmers Weekly]

Supernumerary teats
Some heifers are born with more than four teats. The extra can be removed quite easily with a pair of sharp, curved, surgical scissors before the calf is three weeks old (two weeks is better). The scissors must be properly sterilised first and you could use a local anaesthetic.

CALF HEALTH

The mortality rates for calves up to the age of six months are something like 6–8%. Of those deaths about threequarters occur in the first month of life, and more than a third of those are in the very first week. Many more calves will suffer some form of ill-health and, though they may survive, they will be set back and could cost a fortune in veterinary bills as well. Talk to the vet about preventive measures, including vaccination.

Housed calves, especially those being artificially reared, are at far greater risk than outdoor or suckled calves. The housing itself is a haven for pathogens and the inevitable crowding within housing makes contagion highly likely.

The greatest enemy of a young calf is the bacterial species *Escherichia coli*, commonly referred to as '*E. coli*'. These microscopic forms of life are omnipresent, and at least five hundred strains have been identified so far. Some of them cause no problems at all; others are only a threat to calves whose defences have already been weakened (especially by stress or poor nutrition); and then there are strains which are extremely virulent and knock everything in their path for six, especially if they are unwittingly given conditions in which they can thrive and multiply.

When the newborn calf first emerges from the womb, it is for a brief while free of *E. coli* for the only time in its life, but the bacteria will soon find their way into its intestines. The new calf is undefended; it is born without any gammaglobulin in its body, and gammaglobulin is the protein which contains antibodies – antibodies against all sorts of pathogens, including *E. coli*. Those antibodies are quickly made available to the calf through its mother's colostrum.

But the calf's mother, and therefore her colostrum, can only provide antibodies effective against the particular strains of *E. coli* she has experienced in her own environment. As soon as the calf is transferred to an alien environment, it will meet new bacterial strains against which its defences are very limited indeed. It will also introduce its home strains into that new environment, to the distress of the resident calves.

Most strains are not particularly malignant and indeed some are essential to the calf's digestive processes. But if a calf's resistance is low, even the non-virulent strains can cause problems. Resistance is weakened substantially by stress, and stress in young calves is frequently the result of traumatic events like separation from the mother, travel, exposure in the market, less than kind handling and alien surroundings – many of which have been experienced by bought-in calves even before they come face to face with new routines and new feeding methods in their new, bacteria-laden environment. The very young calf, in particular, can be put under severe stress by environmental and social disturbances in its first few days of life and these tend to result in fatigue, which lowers its general resistance and makes it especially vulnerable to specific pathogens.

If, on top of all this, the calf is fed in such a way that it gets indigestion, large lumps of undigested food will find their way into the large intestine and are manna from heaven for all the resident bacteria, including *E.coli*, which feed greedily and multiply with enthusiasm. All that bacterial activity causes an increase in osmotic pressure in the intestine which leads to the excretion of large amounts of water in the calf's faeces. That is to say, it has diarrhoea – it scours.

The lessons from this little scenario are:
* Avoid a build-up of *E.coli* in calf housing.

Cows for the Smallholder

* Avoid stress.
* Avoid indigestion.

Indigestion in calves is usually caused by overfeeding (too much too quickly in any single feed), irregular feeding, food at the wrong temperature or food at inconsistent temperatures.

Scouring

A suckled calf may scour if the cow is giving too much milk. The diarrhoea is usually yellow and the calf should be taken off the cow for twenty-four hours and given two feeds of glucose and egg (four or five tablespoons of glucose and a beaten raw egg in a couple of litres of warm water for each feed). Then restrict its suckling to three minutes at a time, three times a day, for the next three days. It should clear up quite easily.

If the calf is being artificially raised it'll be worse. At the first sign of scouring, isolate the calf immediately in case the problem is infectious, which it probably is. The calf might have an arched back and tucked-up tummy and it will look generally miserable and poorly. The very liquid dung will be whitish or grey, with perhaps a yellow tinge, and it will smell sickly sweet at first and then sour and horrible. This is 'white scour' – the *E.coli* type. The calf's ears and tail may be icy to the touch and if you do not take action quickly it will become prostrate, dehydrated and anaemic: its eyes will look sunken and the inside of its mouth will be cold and clammy, and it will soon be too late to save it.

Put the isolated calf in a straw 'igloo' with an infra-red lamp if possible. Reduce its feed intake immediately: miss out the next feed or two and then give a glucose-and-egg feed or mix a tablespoon of glucose to a pint of blood-heat water with a teaspoonful of salt. Do *not* use sugar instead of glucose: calves cannot digest sugar. Feed the solution three times a day, giving perhaps a litre or a pint and a half at each feed, or give its usual type of milk substitute but at quarter strength. Call the vet as soon as possible to advise on medication such as antibiotics, astringents and electrolytic fluids to combat the effects of dehydration as quickly as possible. Have faecal swabs available for laboratory analysis, then the vet can decide on the best specific treatment within twenty-four hours. Once the calf's condition begins to improve, you can gradually add milk or milk substitute to its feed, increasing the strength little by little.

Another aggressive organism is *Salmonella*, which can lead to yellow or dark scouring which is often bloodstained. This one can hit even the healthiest of calves up to about six weeks old, and the death rate is as much as 50%, after severe emaciation and pneumonia. Various strains of *Salmonella* can be spread through the dung of carrier cows or by vermin, and the organism is often brought on to the holding by bought-in stock –

calves, recovered cows, pigs, poultry and human beings. The germ can live in dirty buildings or vehicles for several *years* and can be fatal to adult cattle as well as to calves. It is possible to vaccinate against the bacteria but, like *E.coli*, there are many different strains and it is difficult to know which one you are vaccinating against.

A calf with *Salmonella* scour will have inflamed intestines and stomach, a temperature of perhaps 40°C, and of course diarrhoea. Some will quickly develop pneumonia and you need the vet immediately. Old-fashioned remedies like chalk, eggs, kaolin or brandy could be tried while the vet is on the way. It is essential to locate and deal with the source of the infection.

Certain viruses are also associated with scouring in calves up to the age of about two months. The most likely source of infection is adult cattle and it can spread either through their dung or indirectly by means of humans and equipment. These viral diseases are by no means limited to housed calves; they can be quite severe in sucklers at pasture. Affected calves scour and the disease spreads quickly to other calves, especially those a few days old. It may be mild or fatal and there are at present no effective vaccines.

A few years ago a Frenchman wrote to *Farmers Weekly* thus: 'My Uncle had two billy-goats and noticed that their presence in the stable stopped abortions in heifers and cows. We tried them with the calves and for three years we have not had scouring. Perhaps it is the smell, which is stronger in summer, which effects the cure.'

Respiratory problems

Like the digestive system, the calf's respiratory system is susceptible to stress caused by environmental factors, especially in housing, and, like digestive disorders, respiratory diseases are often contagious, frequently expensive to treat and sometimes fatal.

The main problem is *viral pneumonia*, sometimes mild but sometimes severe and leading to death within hours. Many viruses can be responsible and many different bacteria may get in on the act once the initial virus has set the scene. Husbandry and good hygiene are key factors in avoiding respiratory illnesses, which run riot in humid, overcrowded housing and can also be triggered off by chills, draughts, poor ventilation, and general poor hygiene whether indoors or in a crowded yard.

Typical symptoms of the more virulent pneumonias include rapid breathing and gasping for air with the neck outstretched, a dry cough and perhaps a fever, with bacterial complications leading to discharges from the calf's eyes and nostrils. The calf may grind its teeth, which is a typical bovine reaction to pain and discomfort. Isolate the victim immediately and call the vet: you will need antibiotics to combat the bacteria and you will then be in for a long period of nursing to get the calf through the disease. Its lungs are likely to be damaged permanently even then.

Coughing can also be a symptom of *lungworm*, or husk, also known as parasitic bronchitis. This is caused by nematode worms, which live in pasture. The larvae hatch from dung passed by infected cattle; they live in the damp grass until they are eaten by the unsuspecting grazer, then they find their way into the host's lungs where they complete their lifecycle. Young stock in particular may be severely affected: they lose their appetite, their coats stare, their coughs grow worse, they may develop nasal discharges and in the worst cases they may die.

Worms are worms, whether they go for the gut or for the lungs, and the rule is that young animals should only be grazed on clean pasture which has not been used by any other cattle (not even calves) for at least twelve months. The youngsters should anyway be vaccinated before turn-out. Talk to your vet about timing and dosage and think well ahead because the usual dosage is in two batches from four to six weeks apart.

Navel ill or joint ill

The calf's navel can be an open door to bacteria. A newborn calf's navel string must be dressed with iodine etc. (as already described) but that is not necessarily the end of the matter. Wet and dirty rearing pens easily lead to infection, as can cross-suckling by other calves which have a go at their neighbours' navels as substitutes for udders.

Navel ill usually affects young calves, perhaps seven to ten days old, but it can also affect older ones up to perhaps one month old. The initial symptoms may include a puffy navel which develops abscesses and these eventually burst and weep with pus and blood. The calf walks stiffly and becomes listless, breathing quite fast, running a slight temperature and giving little grunts and groans of discomfort. The poisons can spread to its limbs and affect its joints, particularly the knees and hocks, which become swollen, hot and painful. There is quite a high risk of death at this stage and any that do recover will never really be fit; they tend to remain susceptible to all kinds of diseases.

Veterinary treatment is essential and will normally include lancing of the abscesses and a course of antibiotics. In future you will no doubt be more careful about navel-dressing and there is no harm in dressing the newborn calf three times in its first day, twice on its second and twice again on its third, especially if it has been taken away from its mother. Also ensure that bedding and housing are clean.

Lead Poisoning

Calves are eager to learn and they have an endless capacity to lick or chew things which do them no good at all. For this reason they are at great risk from lead poisoning. They *will* lick at flaking paintwork, especially in older buildings, or out in the yard they will explore old paint tins and all sorts of objects and materials which, years ago, someone treated with a lead-based preservative.

Get rid of every trace of peeling paint in a calf house, including up on the ceiling under decades of cobwebs. Flakes can so easily float down to calf level. The symptoms of lead poisoning are unpleasant and alarming: blindness is specific, and there will also be staggering, clambering up walls, frothing at the mouth, bellowing, convulsions and fits and, pretty quickly, death. Act fast. While someone is summoning the vet, give a drench of six beaten raw eggs, or 15g Epsom salts in 285ml water. Repeat at half-hourly intervals for three or four drenches and pray that the vet arrives in time.

There are, of course, other problems which can affect calves but with luck you will never see even the more common ones described above. 'Luck' is the wrong word: the great majority of calf problems can be deterred if you avoid pathogenic build-ups in housing by regularly emptying and thoroughly cleansing and disinfecting the quarters, and avoid causing unnecessary stress to any calf in any way, and are sensible and methodical about feeding. But good luck, anyway.

VIII

HEALTH

'The first step in civilisation was made by the herdsman, we are told, and we may add that the methods pursued by many are still primitive. Between coddling and carelessness there is a happy mean . . . Cattle have a marvellous capacity for accommodating themselves to circumstances, and become able to bear all sorts of neglect and ill-usage, but they do not give the same return, and a good farmer will provide his cattle with all the comfort he can. Rough treatment does not pay.'
[*Horses, Dogs, Birds, Cattle: Accidents & Ailments*, 1904]

If you know your cows, you will be sensitive to any signs of low spirits, discomfort or ill health at an early stage. A healthy cow has a moist muzzle but not a runny nose; her eyes are full rather than either staring or sunken and she takes a general interest in life but has an easy-going attitude to it as long as routines remain familiar. Her breath smells pleasant; her milk yield, the major barometer of health, is fairly predictable; her milk smells like fresh milk and nothing else, and is free of clots or flakes or blood or pus. Her coat has a bloom to it, especially the new spring coat glinting in the sunshine; she keeps herself groomed and her skin is soft, pliable and smooth. Her temperature is somewhere around 38–39°C, though individuals do vary under different conditions.

An anxious cow betrays her distress with her eyes as much as anything else. Rapid and unceasing eye movements are a sign of anxiety, and conversely a very fixed, staring look with the ears held back and nostrils slightly flared indicates distress or pain or sickness. If she is in considerable pain, she will roll her eyes, flare her nostrils wide, push out her head and neck and start groaning. The classic symptom of a sick cow is that she stands alone with her head and neck held low and she may well fail to react to your shouts or your gesticulations, as if she was unaware of you. This is a typical reaction to great stress, and stress of one kind or another can often precipitate illness in an animal by predisposing the animal to succumb to disease.

The more common cow diseases – their symptoms, causes and treatment

– are considered individually later in this chapter. Many of them are avoidable with good husbandry, sound hygiene, sensible precautions, proper nutrition and avoidance of undue stress – and that includes not demanding too much of your cows in terms of productivity. Human greed (sometimes known as sound commercial practice) causes bovine distress. The catalogue of diseases must not alarm you: you may very well have the luck never to witness any of them, especially if your farming methods are less than intensive. But, just in case, it is as well to know what *might* happen.

First of all there are some routine husbandry practices which, if conscientiously carried out, should help avoid some of the problems. The first concerns those basic and often overlooked essentials, feet. The neglect of cows' feet causes more discomfort and considerably more losses (in milk yield, fertility and goodness knows what else) than most farmers realise; indeed lameness is the third most common major problem in our national dairy herd, coming hard on the heels (so to speak) of infertility and mastitis.

FEET

The aims of regular foot-care are to keep the cow's feet healthy and free from disease, and also to keep them sensibly trimmed so that her posture is correct and her weight is evenly balanced when she stands and moves. Correct trimming can in fact both prevent and cure foot disease.

The 'claws' of a cow's foot have two major functions: they protect the living quick of the foot and they carry the full bodyweight of the cow.

The 'wall' of the claw or hoof is like a human nail: it grows continuously from the top, at the coronet (which is like a human cuticle), and new tissue gradually moves down the hoof until it becomes the weight-bearing edge and is eroded by daily wear and tear. The wall edges (mostly the outer rather than inner edge) and part of the heel horn are the weight-bearing areas of each claw, though on natural grazing surfaces some of the weight is also taken by the sole. Most of the horn growth is at the front of the claw and the bodyweight of a cow with overgrown toe-nails rocks back towards her heels, with an inevitable distortion in posture which puts the quick under pressure. This is the main cause of lameness. Regular walks on a level hard surface like dry concrete will help keep the toe-nails of housed cows in check but prolonged contact with unforgiving surfaces is unnatural and causes stress.

Between the claws there is an area of hairless interdigital skin which can easily become inflamed from long periods of standing in warm, damp straw or persistently damp and dirty conditions (mud, slurry etc.), or from mechanical damage.

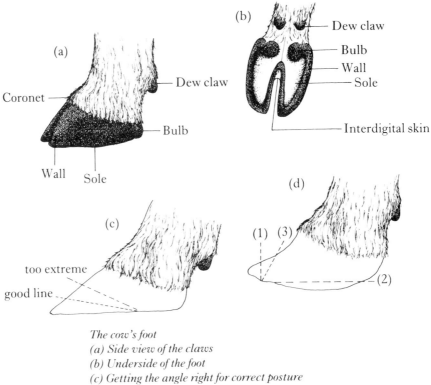

The cow's foot
(a) Side view of the claws
(b) Underside of the foot
(c) Getting the angle right for correct posture
(d) Typical misshapen hoof – the trimming sequence:
    (1) Take off the overgrown tip
    (2) Level the weightbearing walls
    (3) Pare back to a good angle

Foot trimming

Trimming should be a twice-yearly routine if possible, especially a month or six weeks before calving and in the autumn before housing. Take a look at the cow's feet on the ground first: check the shape and length of each claw and assess them for good balance.

You can work blacksmith fashion, resting her leg on your knee, but you must let her know what is going on. Keep your body in contact with hers to reassure her and also to give yourself advance warning of her movements. If you cannot trust her to co-operate, use ropes to raise the leg to a convenient working level.

If you are trimming a lame cow, deal with the lame foot first so that she can stand more comfortably on it while you do the other foot. Use pincers for the harder wall-horn at first, then a sharp horn-knife to pare it off and to deal with the softer areas of horn.

ABOVE: *Example of a Dexter in need of hoof trimming*

RIGHT: *How to hold and pare an overgrown hoof.* [Farmers Weekly]

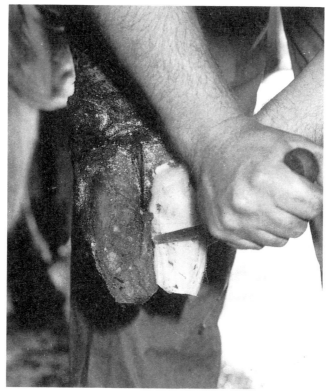

Cows for the Smallholder

The first cut should be to reduce excess tip-length at the front of an *inner* claw. Then you can cut the outer claw to the same length as the inner. Next, reduce the long wall if necessary: pare the inner claw first, with the hoof-knife, aiming to create a flat weight-bearing surface at right angles to the long axis of the shin bone when the cow is standing. Then pare the outer claw, but not too much. Make sure that the wall of the hoof remains high enough to protect the sole, which has a very thin layer of horn and should be pared carefully so that it is concave and is not subject to bruising.

Foot disease

Regular footbaths are a sensible precaution against all foot diseases (weekly for a valuable dairy herd) not only to kill germs but also to toughen vulnerable skin, and a daily walk over a thin bed of lime can help too. Be careful to keep a formalin bath well away from an infected foot, however, as it is much too caustic.

With all foot diseases, it is important to obtain a proper veterinary diagnosis so that treatment can be specific.

Laminitis is a metabolic disorder which affects the formation of horn, particularly in the hind claws, so that the feet become increasingly tender. Poor housing can trigger it off and it is often associated with too much steaming up in the pre-calving period. The symptoms are acute and sudden lameness (often in all the feet), sweating, pain, heat in the hoof, and a preference for lying down. Cold-water footbaths will relieve the pain, but to avoid permanent damage you must seek immediate veterinary aid.

Foul in the foot is caused by *Fusobacterium necrophorum* and complicated by other bacteria. It enters the tissues through tiny injuries and cracks; the foot swells and becomes hot and painful. The cow loses her appetite and may run a temperature, and if the problem is not treated quickly the foot becomes pus-laden, especially between the claws, and a deep wound will form. The first indication of trouble is usually sudden lameness and you will be able to see the swelling, especially just above the coronet. Prevention is by means of good hygiene and the avoidance of injury in the yard, housing and fields: check regularly for debris. Standing in mud or slurry soon leads to cracked feet which are ripe for infection. Bathe the affected foot in *mild* disinfectant, rest the cow as much as possible and ask the vet to take a look.

If a cow develops blisters on her feet and in her mouth – panic! It is probably *foot-and-mouth disease*.

HORNS

In some breeds, especially Longhorns, horns can grow in awkward directions and threaten to curve right into the cheek. Use a cheesewire to take off the tip little by little, cutting it back very gradually because, like a nail or a claw, horns do have a living quick. Sharp horns which endanger other cows (and people) can have their tips filed with a hacksaw and rasp at regular intervals. In some countries it is common practice to fix knobs on horn tips, which are decorative as well as protective.

A broken or over-trimmed horn will pour out blood at an alarming rate. Staunch the flow with a wad of clean cotton-wool or cloth. It is useful to keep a horn styptic handy – a special powder which is used when cows are dehorned in maturity rather than disbudded as calves. This later dehorning must be done under local anaesthetic and with veterinary assistance, and it should not be done during summer when flies will be attracted to the wounds even though they have been cauterised. It can be a messy business with blood gushing out in many cases, and it is far better to disbud the animal when it is a calf.

EYES

A watery eye could be the first sign of a fly-borne disease like *New Forest Eye*. Treat it early because the subsequent stages are a bloodshot look, like pink-eye in humans, followed by the alarming development of a cloudy film which spreads gradually across the eye, turning it bluish-white and blind. The disease can spread quickly in a herd, carried from one eye to another on the feet of flies. The vet will advise you about suitable antibiotic applications direct to the eye.

To remove a piece of chaff from a cow's eye, put a little eye-ointment on your finger so that the chaff sticks to it and can be lifted away.

UDDERS AND TEATS

The udder is, if you like, the focal point of the cow. It is the source of all your potential wealth from her and the udder of a milking cow, whether dairy cow or suckler, works hard and works constantly. It should be respected and valued. A lot can go wrong with it if you are careless, ham-fisted or less than scrupulous with hygiene.

By the very nature of their shape, position and lack of protection, udders are prone to accident – they get trodden on, gashed by wire, butted by horns, and scraped by the teeth of a persistent calf. Any cuts and wounds should be dealt with promptly to keep bacteria and flies out. Injured teats can cause havoc at milking time but in most cases a good dollop of udder cream and some sympathetic hand-milking will enable you to relieve the affected quarter. Any cow with an udder infection should be milked after all the others to avoid spreading the problem.

Cracked or chapped teats interfere with milking and are likely candidates for infection. Always make sure teats are thoroughly dry after milking and smear them with an ointment based on magnesium carbonate or zinc oxide and cod-liver oil, from your local chemist.

Newly calved cows might develop a 'pea in the teat' – a little obstruction in the milk canal which impedes the flow and makes milking awkward. It needs surgical removal by the vet. Warts can also interfere with milking and are best treated by means of injection: you should consult your vet. Herbal cures include rubbing the warts with the fluffy insides of broad-bean pods.

Scabby sores can be caused by fungi (e.g. Blackspot), viral infections or bacteria, and treatment usually includes antibiotics but it is important to have the problem accurately diagnosed first. Some of the conditions can infect people as well as other cows.

Mastitis

Mastitis is the most common udder problem of all. There are several kinds and degrees of mastitis, and most of them are a sign of bad husbandry – poor hygiene, damage to teats or udder, dirty equipment, too much steaming up, damp and dirty housing, summer flies attacking dry cows and heifers, and, above all, *bad milking techniques*, especially with machine milking.

Mastitis always arises from some initial injury or soreness becoming infected by bacteria and possibly viruses. Some forms are highly contagious and some can kill. Older cows seem to suffer most and there may also be a genetic predisposition. The first month of a lactation is the period of greatest risk.

The symptoms of acute mastitis are a hot, swollen udder with painful teats, a noticeable drop in yield, general lack of appetite and interest, perhaps a temperature, and, characteristically, clots in the foremilk strippings.

If you do find clots or perhaps blood in the foremilk and notice that one or more quarters are hot and swollen, take immediate steps to treat the cow and to avoid the spread of infection. Milk the affected cow after any others, preferably by hand to avoid contaminating machinery. Massage her udder with warm cloths or warm udder cream. Milk her every two hours or so to ease the pressure as well as giving any specific treatment recommended by the vet. Inject mammary antibiotics gently into the teat canal after milking, and thereafter discard her milk for several days as instructed by the manufacturers of the treatment. Never stop giving antibiotics before the course is completed.

Find out *why* the cow has mastitits: look first at the milking parlour. Check all parts of the milking machinery (especially teat liners and pulsators) to make sure they are working correctly and efficiently and are thoroughly clean throughout, and never leave a cluster on the cow for too long. Be aware that infection can spread directly through the milk or indirectly by means of your hands or clothing, or udder cloths and other equipment, or by direct udder-skin contact between cows, and that the bacteria can live happily in housing and yards, with a special liking for sawdust bedding. Always clean every cow's teats before milking, whether or not you are aware of mastitis; use a separate, sterilised udder cloth or disposable paper towel for each different cow; dip every teat in a recognised teat disinfectant after every milking; use intramammary antibiotics after the last milking when a cow is dried off (and thoroughly clean the teat first to avoid shoving bacteria up the canal along with the applicator); and follow all these procedures strictly, every single milking, for ever, even if you have no reason to suspect mastitis. Do not let your initial good resolutions slip.

Summer mastitis often produces a lot of stinking pus and can ruin an affected quarter for life; it can also be lethal and is a case for immediate veterinary attention. To avoid it, avoid flies. They are probably at their worst in hot, thundery weather in low-lying fields enclosed by high hedges and trees that afford very little air movement. Dry cows and heifers are particularly susceptible: give them fly-repellent ear tags, check their udders daily to make sure that they are neither damaged by tiny fly bites or cross-suckling nor bag up too soon or too tightly. An early sign of trouble might be lameness, caused by the discomfort of an infected teat. You can seal the teats of dry cows with a special permeable and non-irritant tape or a protective coating of Stockholm tar as well as using dry-cow therapy. Act fast if you see a down-calver looking distressed, especially if she has a hard quarter: summer mastitis can poison the cow's whole system and it can kill. Call the vet and then start massaging and stripping out her udder while you wait. You want to draw out as much of the poison as possible.

Gangrene mastitis. If a cow's udder feels hard and *cold*, she could have gangrene mastitis which cuts off the blood supply to a quarter and chokes it to death.

CATTLE DISEASES AND PROBLEMS

(Notifiable diseases, zoonoses and eradication schemes are given in the Appendix.)

Abortion

Certain diseases in the pregnant cow may lead to abortion or stillbirth and might also lead to calf abnormalities. The first reaction to abortion should be to isolate the cow until you know what caused it; burn any afterbirth, discharge and bedding as a precaution. Brucellosis used to be the most common cause of abortion and it is still necessary to test aborting cows to rule out this possibility. It is highly contagious and can also infect humans, in whom it assumes all kinds of unsuspected guises – undulant fever, arthritis, depression and 'flu-like symptoms, for example. Leptospirosis now causes more abortions in cows.

Acetonaemia or ketosis

Acetonaemia can be avoided by sound feeding. Although it is claimed that this glucose-deficiency problem usually affects only high-yielding dairy cows (especially high-butterfat breeds) given too much protein or cereals, it can equally affect the humble housecow in some areas and is sometimes seen as an emergency through which the cow will be lucky to live. Over-steaming, starvation, stress, too much kale, too much butyric silage, too much protein, deficient pasture – all these have been suggested as factors in acetonaemia. It strikes when a cow is in a negative energy balance, especially and crucially if she is short of metabolic glucose precursors and has to use body reserves of ketones instead of glucose for energy. Glucose in her bloodstream is heavily drawn upon for the foetus, especially late in the pregnancy, and when she does calve she also needs glucose to supply lactose in milk.

Symptoms include low milk yield, definite lack of appetite (especially for concentrates), and perhaps hard dung or diarrhoea and depression. The identifying sign is the characteristically sweet 'pear-drops' smell of ketones on her breath. There is a greater tendency for the disease to develop if the cow has been kept indoors on less than adequate hay and dry foods and too little exercise. A dramatic cure was effected by one vet who turned a Jersey housecow out into the mid-winter snow to find herself some greenstuff. She chose ivy, and she survived. A couple of tablespoonfuls of molasses in the steam-up ration might be a useful preventive. Some cows recover spontaneously as their milk yield drops or react quite quickly to a drench of molasses in warm water, glycerine or glucose precursors (but not glucose itself) but others need anabolic steroids or vitamin B injections.

Bloat

This can be quite a problem if cattle are grazing lush (i.e. low-fibre) or frosted grass, or grass with plenty of clover in it, or frosted kale and turnips. Bloat is a build-up of gases (carbon dioxide and methane) in the rumen which blow it up like a balloon: you will see a decided bulge near the left flank. The pressure can be enormous, and the aim is to relieve it one way or another. The problem is that the animal cannot belch in the normal way but you might be able to encourage belching if you keep the animal on its feet and on the move – but do not excite it or you will make matters worse. Give drenches of silicone-based bloat mixtures, or raw linseed oil mixed with turps (*not* turpentine substitute), or any vegetable oil with warm water, or margarine, or washing soda in warm water, but be cautious with drenching and do not stress the patient.

If none of this helps, and the pressure continues to build, the animal could soon succumb to respiratory distress and might collapse. The vet should be summoned and may need to take the drastic action of releasing the gas by literally puncturing the rumen at the highest point of the bloat with a sharp trochar, using a cannula to keep the hole open while the gas escapes. Do not try this yourself unless you have experience, and make sure nobody is smoking while the operation is performed: it is quite possible to ignite the escaping methane!

If the bloat is caused by dry food like grain, you could relieve it with a stomach tube carefully introduced through the mouth and down the throat. You will know if you have reached the right place by the unmistakable smell of the gas but you must make sure you do not push the tube into the lungs by mistake. Ideally keep a special stomach tube on the holding but in an emergency the kind of tube used in home wine-making could be a useful substitute.

Bloat can be avoided by sensible grazing management, especially at spring turn-out. Arrange spring grazing so that the cattle cannot gobble too much too quickly: give limited areas of grass (and avoid clover-rich pasture) and feed some hay or a little dried sugarbeet pulp beforehand. Devise ways of keeping them moving during the day. Use a special anti-bloat mineral block (basically magnesium disguised with dried black treacle). Avoid the practice of putting the cows out for only an hour or two at first because any cow with half a mind soon realises what is going on and promptly crams in as much grass as she can, like a drinker trying to beat closing time. The spring turn-out is such a time of joy – even the most matronly cow will kick up her heels and gallop across the grass, her udder swinging crazily. Make sure that it remains a joy, not a gluttonous disaster.

Calving and post-calving problems

Retention of afterbirth is perhaps the most common post-calving problem. The cow fails to 'cleanse' within two or three days after calving, or may wander around with half the placenta hanging out behind for a few days. In the latter case, leave it alone for perhaps four days (you can trim it off at hock-level if it is trailing in the dirt, but leave a good length protruding) and then call in a professional to deal with it. Never try to yank it out yourself: you could cause considerable damage and the cow may never conceive again. The placenta is attached to the uterus by cotyledon 'buttons' and the expert will very gently ease the afterbirth away from each button, one by one.

Eversion of the uterus is a more serious problem, not to be confused with a dangling afterbirth. The placenta is thin and stringy, whereas the uterus is a huge, heavy red bulk. This is an emergency: call the vet at once and explain what has happened, then tie the cow up and try to keep the uterus clean and protected from damage while you wait. If it is a recurring problem it may be due to calcium deficiency which causes the uterine muscles to lose tone.

Displaced abomasum is a common problem in some areas. This stomach usually rests on the floor of the abdomen on the right-hand side but may be displaced during the early stages of labour and end up at the left flank or behind the left-hand rib-cage, where it looks a little like bloat and 'pings' like a tight drum if you tap it. The necessary veterinary operation is quite simple and the cow will have nothing to show for it but a few stitches.

Post-calving paralysis may or may not resolve itself after a few days. It is usually due to pressure on pelvic nerves during calving which deprives the cow of the use of her hind-legs so that they splay out, and down she goes. Keep her propped up on her brisket with straw bales; rub her back just behind the ribs with liniment and keep her warm with sacking; give her a drench of Epsom salts in cold water, and ask the vet about tonics or cortisones. Time, rest and patience are usually the best cures. But make sure it is not milk fever (see below), which needs very urgent treatment.

Dietary deficiencies
Mineral deficiencies or excesses are responsible for many problems – for example hypomagnesaemia, milk fever, infertility, anaemia, kidney and bladder problems, jaundice or general debility. Vitamin deficiencies can affect the brain and may cause blindness.

Have your soil analysed for minerals and the livestock blood-sampled for a metabolic profile of the herd. Mineral licks or additives can be a boon if you know what is lacking, and bought-in products can supplement home-grown deficiencies. Pasture management is important: over-liming can create deficiencies in copper and cobalt, and too much nitrogen can render several minerals unavailable to the plants and hence to the cows. Both magnesium and calcium suffer if pasture is overdressed with potash or if N levels are too high.

Digestive problems
The main signs of digestive upsets are that the cow stops cudding and may express pain by constantly looking back along her flank, kicking at her stomach and sometimes grinding her teeth. Cattle may scour after a sudden change in their diet, or because of eating musty or frosted food, or eating too much of anything, or being given an excess of slightly poisonous substances like sugarbeet tops. Or they might have worms; or be allergic to

a particular plant. More seriously, diarrhoea may be a symptom of Johnes disease (if it is full of bubbles) or some other disease. Your vet can supply anti-diarrhoea mixtures and suggest the quickest way of replacing lost fluids.

Constipation can also be a sign of disease or might indicate an impacted rumen which can be relieved with exercise, lots of drinking water and a friendly pummelling of the flank. Linseed oil, ginger or Epsom salts in water will ease the situation. Good laxatives are a bran mash (add some molasses or linseed cake to make it more palatable) or drenches of black treacle in warm water, medicinal liquid paraffin or castor oil. Laxative diets include molasses, golden syrup (which calves love), yeast, oatmeal gruel, warm fresh milk, hay tea and pulped carrots.

Enzootic bovine leucosis (EBL)
EBL is caused by a virus and can be spread by direct contact or by means of faeces, urine, afterbirth, milk, ticks and biting insects, and instruments for ear-punching, dehorning and injections. It is a notifiable disease which causes multiple tumours and can lead to leukaemia. Herds should be tested regularly (it frequently hides in a herd without any obvious symptoms) and you should never buy in stock from unattested herds.

Hypomagnesaemia, grass staggers or tetany
Subnormal levels of magnesium in the bloodstream can cause problems, particularly in dairy cows on lush spring or autumn grass or silage. Newly calved cows are at greatest risk. Magnesium is not readily stored in the cow, and its excretion in urine and milk needs to be balanced by regular intake from the diet. Preventive measures are simple and worthwhile: add calcined magnesite to the ration during the danger period (starting *before* turn-out), or dose with magnesium 'bullets'. Avoid over-fertilising pasture and treat it with Epsom salts (magnesium sulphate).

The symptoms of staggers are described in its common name. The cow is nervous and excitably alert to unusual noises or strangers; she trembles, shivers violently, her ears may twitch, her eyes roll and her lids flicker, and in acute cases she may stagger and fall in a fit of spasms, with kicking legs and frothing mouth. Act quickly but be *very* gentle and quiet with her, avoiding any excitement or additional stress. Treatment is an immediate injection of magnesium.

Infectious bovine rhinotracheitis (IBR)
IBR is caused by a herpes virus which can affect cattle of any age and can lead to respiratory disease, abortion, vulvovaginitis or, in a young calf, encephalitis. It is possibly more common in beef herds, especially if housed in winter.

Early symptoms are loss of appetite and a high fever for several days, with a characteristic dirty discharge from eyes and nose, salivation and a soft cough. Pneumonia may complicate the situation. Damage by the virus can so inflame the upper airways that the animal literally chokes to death. Another form of the disease is genital rather than respiratory and an infected bull can continue to pass on the virus in his semen for the rest of his life. Many recovered cattle remain carriers, so that if they are transferred to a 'clean' herd they can trigger off an outbreak of the disease. Control is by vaccination, or by testing and culling.

Infertility

Infertility is a major cause of economic loss in herds. It may be due to the female's failure to conceive or it may be entirely the fault of the bull. Diet plays an important part in fertility, and carbohydrate deficiency in high-yielding cows is a factor to consider. Mineral deficiencies and parasites can contribute to a general lack of thrift which can lead to infertility. Manganese deficiency in particular is a cause of of anoestrus.

The most common causes are cystic ovaries, sometimes hereditary or due to trace-element deficiencies, and stress brought on by demanding a high milk yield at a comparatively low plane of nutrition. Talk to your vet about up-to-date hormone therapy.

Leptospirosis

There are several kinds of leptospiral organisms and those that affect cattle are the hardjo leptospires, which breed in the kidneys and are spread through urine, semen etc. Symptoms of hardjo in cows include dramatic drops in milk yield and the development of a 'flabby bag' (a sudden drop in yield from all four quarters and the bag looks as if it has already been milked out; also, the milk which does emerge is often thick and yellow, with or without clots or blood in it).

More common than flabby bag is abortion and the hardjo bacteria are now responsible for more cow abortions than any other disease in this country. Abortions occur up to twelve weeks after infection and are most common during the final three months of the pregnancy. Veterinary attention is essential. The bacteria can also infect humans (the symptoms are like those of 'flu) and a vaccine has been developed to protect people who might be vulnerable. It often starts as a blinding headache and if it is not quickly diagnosed and treated it can easily develop into meningitis. Always let your GP know if you are in contact with livestock, because many doctors would fail to suspect hardjo and you could be in for a long and debilitating illness. The bacteria can survive for long periods in urine-contaminated water. Rats, too, are well-known carriers of leptospirosis: get rid of them.

Milk fever (hypocalcaemia)

When a cow calves and suddenly launches into a lactation after several dry weeks, the demand for extra calcium to replace that lost in her milk output can be excessive and she may go down with milk fever. The problem usually strikes a cow giving birth to her third calf or more, and once she has had milk fever she is likely to repeat the problem annually – and her daughters may also be prone to it.

The main danger period is within forty-eight hours of calving. You might notice an uncomfortable, stiff 'paddling' of the hind legs because the disorder can produce an ascending paralysis which starts in the hind legs and works its way quite quickly to the rest of the body. She will have a general air of disquiet and may become excitable or even violent. Her temperature is more likely to be subnormal than feverish and her ears will feel cold.

The crucial stage is when she becomes a 'downer'. Characteristically, she will lie on her sternum with her head turned into her flank, and it will revert to that position if you try and straighten her kinked neck. She is quite unable to rise and the next stage may well be coma and death. This is an emergency: call the vet immediately you suspect milk fever. If the diagnosis is confirmed, the treatment is an urgent boost of calcium by means of an injection of soluble calcium salts just behind the shoulder.

Prevention is by only partially milking a newly calved cow and by checking the mineral content of her diet. The pre-calving ration should include adequate minerals, especially magnesium, but *not* excess calcium: recent research suggests it might even be better to reduce calcium. It is the ability to *utilise* available calcium which is important. Vitamin D is vital shortly before calving: it is involved with the absorption of calcium and phosphorus. It is of course the 'sunshine' vitamin: direct sunlight on the coat is the best source of all, and there is a little in sun-dried hay but generally none in growing plants. Colostrum, incidentally, contains about ten times as much vitamin D as normal milk. Avoid using poultry manure or excess potash on pasture and hayfields because the potassium interferes with calcium uptake. Do not steam the cow up too much and you might find that a green diet helps – try crushed nettles (valuable food), steamed hay, watercress, watermint and molasses. Magnesium should be included in the ration for the two weeks before calving — either add about 100g of magnesium flakes to the cow's drinking water each day, or sprinkle about 50g of calcined magnesite per cow per day into the dry-cow ration or on the silage.

Poisoning

There is a list of poisons and poisonous plants in the Appendix and if you know or even suspect an animal has eaten any of them you must summon the vet immediately. The symptoms of poisoning include great distress, loss of appetite, salivation, grunting, colic, vomiting (rare in cattle but forceful when it does occur, e.g. after eating rhododendrons), tooth-grinding and belly-kicking because of stomach pains, and ultimately convulsions and death. If an animal is suffering from fits in the later stages, all you can do is try and keep it quiet and see that it does not injure itself; then start praying that the vet will arrive in time. There are certain remedies which you should always have in stock in case they are needed: bran mash (hay chaff, bran and crushed oats scalded with boiling water and kept at body temperature – several bucketfuls), sugar, milk, eggs, yeast; astringents in case of really bad diarrhoea (kaolin powder, chlorodyne, boiled and cooled milk, cold gruels of flour and starch, eggs, or even a drop of whisky). At first do not try and reduce diarrhoea because it is nature's way of flushing out the poisons.

Poisoned cattle never learn and it is more than likely that the victim will develop a craving for the very plant which poisoned it. The craving may be so extreme that it will eat nothing else and will make quite violent efforts to reach the plant.

Skin problems

Allergies can cause skin problems – either in reaction to specific foods or plants, or to sunlight (photosensitivity). The latter might be triggered off by eating certain foods like clover, rape or various weeds, and it could lead to anaemia and general loss of condition. The animal will need to be housed for a while in a darkened building.

Lice are happiest during the dark days of winter, nestling in long winter coats. The victim rubs constantly against anything and everything, gradually wearing away the hair, and you will be able to see the bugs. Take care that any lice powders you use do not affect the milk.

Ringworm is an unsightly and very contagious fungal disease which can also be caught by people. Spores can live for years in old woodwork. The animal develops itchy circular scabby patches which lose hair and look grey, especially on the neck and face. Tincture of iodine, mustard paste or raw lemon juice can help the skin problem and there are various specific sprays and paints which can be applied to affected areas after scrubbing off heavy scabbing. There are oral fungicides too.

Warbles

Warble flies cause cattle to 'gad' – that is, to rush about the field with their tails high trying to escape. The flies lay eggs on their victim's leg-hairs between about May and September (you could try singeing the leg-hairs very carefully to destroy the eggs). The maggots enter bovine body tissues during summer and migrate right through the body, eventually forming swelling lumps on the back during the first six months of the following year. There is a little breathing hole in each lump and sometimes pus. The animal's potential hide is ruined by the holes; its gullet and back flesh are also damaged. The warble fly eradication scheme has been markedly successful but there are still problems in some regions, where dressing between specified dates is enforced, and all cattle owners should keep a sharp eye out for infestations, which are notifiable.

Worms and parasites

There are all sorts of worms which might affect cattle. The main groups are flukes (which go for the liver), tapeworms (in the intestines) and round-worms or nematodes, which become parasites in stomachs, intestines and lungs.

The war against worms is fought in two ways: by regular dosing of the animals and by sensible management of the grazing. Adult cattle tend to develop immunities but can still perpetuate the lifecycle of the parasites, so to avoid infecting young stock keep them off pasture which has been grazed by adult cattle until at least July in the following year. Monitor for worm infestation by having dung samples tested by your vet, who can then tell you whether worming is necessary, and when.

Here's a thought. Apparently certain wormers make dung unattractive to those hosts of small creatures that are supposed to clear up the pats. Could it be that the use of wormers will turn your pasture into one huge, permanent cowpat?

The main problems caused by worms, apart from a general drain on an animal's system and hence a drop in production, are parasitic bronchitis (husk, lungworm), fascioliasis (liverfluke) and parasitic gastro-enteritis. *Redwater* is caused by minute parasites which use the common tick as an intermediary host to spread the mites with its bite. It is a problem in tick-infested rough grazing and bracken land. Local cattle acquire im-munity gradually and the cattle most at risk are adults transferred from districts which are free of the problem. The parasite is a blood one: it enters the red blood cells and breaks them down so that haemoglobin, the red pigment in blood, is released, and symptoms include a distinct red tinge to the urine (hence redwater). It needs prompt veterinary diagnosis and treatment.

NURSING

Drenching

The aim of a drench is to get liquid into an animal's stomach but there is a danger that you might pour the stuff straight into its lungs instead.

Tilt the animal's head up so that its neck is stretched, but make sure that the mouth is no higher than its eye-level or it will choke. Be gentle and calm, because you are probably dealing with a sick animal anyway, and also because an agitated animal will gasp and choke.

Keeping the animal's neck straight, open its mouth by hooking your fingers where there are no teeth at one side and insert the neck of the drenching bottle or gun from the other side. Let the bottle touch the roof of the mouth to warn the animal that something is coming, then its glottal will close over the windpipe to avoid choking. 'Drench' is a misleading word: *trickle* the liquid gradually and carefully down its throat, keeping the neck and head extended in a straight line and raised a few degrees above parallel with the ground. Stroke the throat gently to encourage swallowing, and if the animal coughs or chokes let the head drop immediately. Take care if the bottle is glass (it could easily be chewed): try pulling a piece of rubber piping over the bottleneck, which will protect it and also make it longer so that you can place it further back in the mouth to help swallowing.

How to drench correctly. [Farmers Weekly]

Injections

Before you try and give injections, *please* have a practical demonstration from your vet. Always use sharp, clean needles, and ensure that the skin area surrounding the point of injection is clean as well. Massage the site after an injection has been given: a good rub will disperse the dose and prevent the formation of lumps and abscesses.

Subcutaneous injections are given a few inches behind the shoulder and the dose is injected just under the skin. Clip the hair, swab the site with antiseptic, lift the skin with one hand and slip the needle in at a very acute angle to the body so that it goes under the outer hide but does not penetrate the 'meat'.

Intramuscular injections are given in a fleshy part of the thigh, carefully avoiding bone, or just behind the shoulder. Slap the site once or twice with the heel of your hand to deaden the area, then drive the needle firmly straight into the muscle. Cow-hide is tough: the needle must be sharp and your action resolute. The needle can go in to its full length. Withdraw the plunger slightly: if you see any blood in the tube, you have entered a blood vessel and must try again.

Intravenous injections should only be given by those who have had ample practice. The needle is inserted into the jugular vein.

Intramammary injections are needle-less. Draw off a little milk from the teat, swab its tip with meths or surgical spirit, then carefully insert the nozzle of the infusion tube into the teat canal, making sure that you do not graze or injure it. Squeeze the tube to persuade its contents into the teat.

Pills

The easiest method of giving a pill or bolus to a cow is with a balling gun (well coated with vegetable oil) which is put into the mouth past the hump of the tongue and then the bolus is ejected by means of the gun's plunger.

Taking temperatures

Cattle's temperatures are taken rectally. Make sure the thermometer is clean, then grease it for lubrication. Hold the tail up and insert the thermometer into the rectum – but not so far that you lose it in there (it has happened!). Keep the bulb against the side of the rectum: you want the anal temperature, not that of the faeces. The normal temperature is about 38–39°C.

Wounds

Vinegar or tincture of iodine are useful home remedies for bruises. Witch hazel is a good astringent to reduce bleeding. Cobwebs are good for staunching wounds (a scientific fact, not just an old wives' tale) and black pepper disinfects.

ALTERNATIVES

The use of powerful drugs has become widely accepted throughout agriculture and many farmers automatically reach for the needle if there is a problem with livestock. Modern drugs certainly have their place: they can cure very quickly and they can fight back successfully at diseases which used to be fatal. Antibiotics have saved the lives of countless cows and calves.

But there are those who are wary of this increasing dependence on the drug manufacturers. It seems that, overall, our cattle are increasingly *un*healthy, and in the panic to make a reasonable living it could be that people are not pausing to wonder why that should be. The smallholder, who has a much more personal relationship with livestock than the big farmer can ever hope for, has a chance to stand back a little from the rat-race and consider whether the miracles of science and the commendable labours of those who work in research laboratories are really heading in the right direction after all.

There is a vicious spiral. Cattle are bred, fed and manipulated for maximum productivity. The increased output inevitably causes stress in many forms, some so subtle that we do not recognise them, and the animal succumbs to all kinds of disorders. The disorders are treated with, say, antibiotics; the animal returns to its productive treadmill. But the treatment has only dealt with the *results* of stress; it has done nothing to remove or alleviate the several sources of stress and, inevitably, the animal succumbs again – perhaps to a different disorder, and it is treated, and . . .

Over the last two centuries in particular, breeders have done a magnificent job in 'improving' our livestock but perhaps, all along, our motives and priorities have been wrong. If only we did not demand so much from livestock. If only we had more time to spend in caring for them. If only we did not exploit our livestock in seeking to sustain lifestyles that would be the envy of rich men in earlier centuries.

If the substantial list of problems and diseases discussed in this chapter has made you stop and think, you might well have decided that there must be other ways. And one cannot help feeling that the drugs we pump into the bodies of animals which supply us with our own food must to some degree affect our bodies too – all those antibiotics which we unwittingly absorb from milk and meat, all those worming treatments, and of course all those hormones, which cause such public disquiet, whether groundless or not.

There are alternative treatments, and ways of preventing sickness in the first place by using commonsense and reducing your demands on the animals. If your curiosity about other cures is aroused, read one or two books on herbalism, homoeopathy and similar treatments which depend on attitudes and philosophies as much as actual physical applications: they might open your eyes to a whole new way of life – for you as well as for your cows. Bear in mind that the environment in which a sick animal is cared for is just as important as the medicines with which it is treated, and take its psychological needs into account. Do stop and think about priorities and make a point of reviewing your aims and methods at intervals: it is all too easy to find yourself hurtling along on the train that carries bandwagons for commerce, science, progress and 'more, more, more'. Slow down, and wonder.

IX

MILK

'As to the pretended unwholesomeness of milk in certain cases; as to its not being adapted to some constitutions, I do not believe one word of the matter. Neat cattle will touch nothing that is not wholesome in its nature; nothing that is not wholly innoxious. Out of a pail that has ever had grease in it they will not drink a drop, though they be raging with thirst. Their very breath is fragrance. And how, then, is it possible, that unwholesomeness should distil from the udder of a cow!'

[*Cottage Economy*, William Cobbett, 1823]

Milk is the food of life. It may be largely water but just a pint a day of this magic liquid can give a full-grown man doing a reasonable day's work a quarter of the protein and all the calcium his body needs, plus about half the recommended levels of vitamin C and riboflavin. A gallon would give him nearly all the energy he needs, too. Where would you be without milk?

MILK QUALITY

It is customary to analyse milk in terms of its content of butterfat (BF%) on the one hand and all other solids ('solids-not-fat', or SNF%) on the other. Farmers who sell their milk straight to the MMB are paid on the basis of the total yield of solids, especially protein, lactose and butterfat. The proportions of different constituents in fresh milk, and the total yield of the milk, depend on a wide range of factors and it is the manipulation of these factors which is the art of cow farming.

Genetics is a major factor affecting milk yield and quality, with butterfat content in particular being highly heritable. A higher yield of liquid milk does not necessarily mean a higher yield of nutritious solids, however, and indeed the reverse tends to be the case.

Milk quality is affected by diet: what goes in comes out, albeit altered by the digestive processes along the way. A cow's drinking water, for a start, must be fresh and clean, and preferably free of the heavy doses of chlorine used by some water authorities. Whatever the cow drinks or eats may flavour her milk to some extent and there could be a whole untapped

Fig. xix MILK CONSTITUENTS

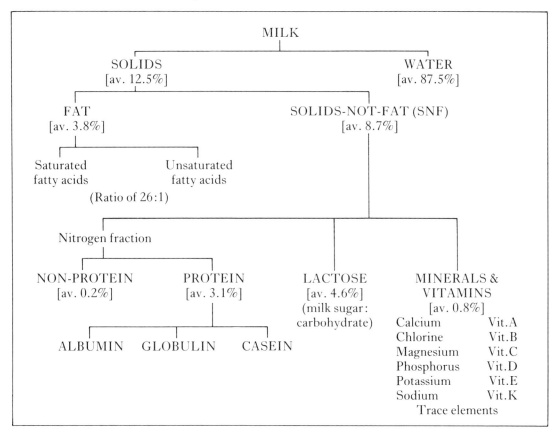

cheese-maker's market for milk flavoured 'in the cow' with the herbs she has grazed!

The protein content of a cow's milk tends to increase if she is fed on legumes. Fibre is crucial for butterfat production (spring grass is low in fibre, and beware of feeding too little hay in proportion to grain in the winter). Mineral content is more difficult to adjust because some minerals may be locked away from the cow by various factors and combinations but in theory root crops and grains should increase the calcium in her milk.

Taints and pollutants

Obviously milk quality can be affected by visible pollutants like muck. Proper parlour routines will help keep the milk as clean as it was in the udder, but milk is easily tainted and just a little tainted milk can

Cows for the Smallholder

Fig. xx FACTORS AFFECTING MILK QUALITY AND QUANTITY

COW	ENVIRONMENT AND MANAGEMENT
Breed and strain	Disease
Age	Season of year
Stage of lactation	Environmental temperature
Individuality	Nutrition
Number of calvings	Water intake
Calving month	Milking intervals and techniques

MILK FAT

STRONG INFLUENCES: breeding, season, fibre in ration, milk yield (inverse proportion), proportions of volatile fatty acids in ration.

INCREASED BY	DECREASED BY
High acetate production in rumen from high levels of hay, silage and dried beet pulp	Low roughage in diet
	High levels of concentrates
	Finely ground roughage
	Leafy spring herbage (low fibre)
Grazing of higher fibre grass-stems	Too much kale and concentrates in autumn and not enough hay
Acetonaemia (ketosis)	Longer overnight milking interval
Temperature greater than 39°C	Failure to strip out udder
	Age of cow (slightly)
Lactation nearing end	Scouring
Calving in good condition	Calving very lean
	Lack of exercise
	Stress
	Three-times-a-day milking (%)
	Very laxative diet
	Foremilk (less fat than strippings)
	Increased milk yield

SOLIDS-NOT-FAT (protein and lactose)

STRONG INFLUENCES: breed, season, stage of lactation.

INCREASED BY	DECREASED BY
Spring turn-out	Long-term underfeeding
Steaming up	Age of cow (after 4th lactation)
Good hay and silage	Mastitis (casein and lactose)
ME intake	Temperature greater than 39°C
May/June grazing	Calving November–February
	Winter season
	Poor body condition

(Increased milk yield increases percentage of lactose but decreases percentage of protein in the milk.)

Fig. xx *(continued)*

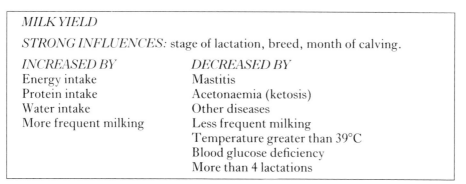

MILK YIELD

STRONG INFLUENCES: stage of lactation, breed, month of calving.

INCREASED BY	*DECREASED BY*
Energy intake	Mastitis
Protein intake	Acetonaemia (ketosis)
Water intake	Other diseases
More frequent milking	Less frequent milking
	Temperature greater than 39°C
	Blood glucose deficiency
	More than 4 lactations

Fig. xxi SEASONAL EFFECTS ON MILK CONSTITUENTS

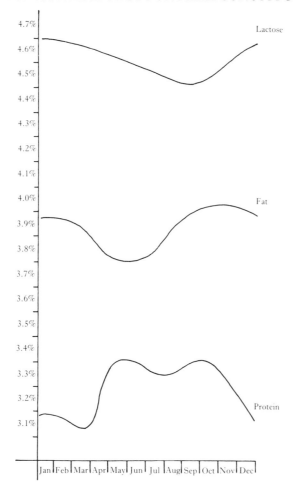

Cows for the Smallholder

Fig. xxii MILK YIELD AND COMPOSITION – BREED COMPARISONS

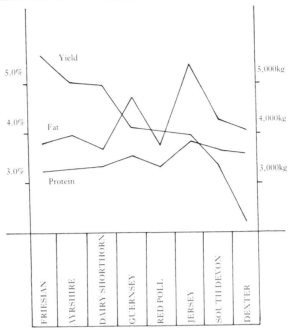

contaminate a very large quantity of milk, butter and cheese if it is mixed into a batch. Some of the more common milk-tainters in a cow's ration are too much kale, turnips and sugarbeet tops and these, as well as butyric silage, should only be fed *after* milking. Wild plants like mayweed, tansy and wild garlic are tainters and so are ration ingredients like fishmeal and distillers' grains.

Taints can also be absorbed from typical parlour and farm chemicals and there is an increasing problem with chlorophenol taints from sterilising fluids, detergents, disinfectants and footbaths. Any product including an ingredient ending in '-ol' could cause problems and you would be well advised to check the contents list on the labels of udder creams, fly sprays and antiseptics used on or near your cows. (A tip: if it turns white in water, it is an '-ol'.) Substances like creosote, bitumen, diesel fuel, paraffin or fresh paint can taint exposed milk without ever touching the stuff: the taints are simply absorbed from the air.

Then there are bacterial taints, which can make affected milk taste sour, fruity, fishy, malty or like caramel. Mastitic milk tends to be salty and in acetonaemia the milk is unpleasantly sweet.

An important potential contaminant is any form of antibiotic treatment which, while it may do a good job on clearing up infections in the cow, will by its nature inhibit the growth of micro-organisms in her milk, and any cheesemaker or yogurt producer using that milk will curse you roundly. So will all those innocent milk-drinkers who are allergic to antibiotics.

If a cow has been treated with antibiotics, residues will flood into the milk and will continue to be present at significant levels for several milkings. This includes antibiotic injections given for ailments which have nothing to do with her milk system, because milk is synthesised from her bloodstream. You *must* adhere to the milk-withholding period recommended by the manufacturer of the antibiotic and make quite sure that any milk from a treated cow is withheld from sale. In your own interests, refrain from giving it to your family too, and be wary of feeding it to other livestock.

The MMB regularly tests milk for antibiotic residues and will penalise producers who fail the test. Bear in mind that one dose of antibiotic in one of your cows could contaminate a whole lorry-load of milk, and the board could levy the full value of that load on you – something like £30,000.

Milk is tested monthly for the presence of brucellosis in the herd and also mastitis by means of a cell count. The boards test the total bacteria count (TBC) of your milk every week as well and you can be penalised if the levels are too high. The test counts the number of micro-organisms per millilitre of milk. Fresh milk is a living substance and is bound to contain some bacteria, however strict your hygiene, and if it did not it would be useless to cheese-makers, but the bacteria count begins to rise the moment the milk leaves the udder – or even sooner if the cow has mastitis. Mastitis, dirty udders and teats, slurry splashes, less-than-clean milking equipment and inadequate cooling in the bulk tank all add their quota to the bacteria count. Again, these are problems which can be avoided by good parlour practice and should be borne in mind whether you are milking a huge herd or just one housecow. In the old days, most milkers never touched the stuff themselves: they knew only too well what was in it besides the milk! Even today some farmers will blithely fill their bulk tanks with milk they themselves consider unfit to drink.

'About this time they would hear Dairyman Crick's voice, lecturing the non-resident milkers for arriving late, and speaking sharply to old Deborah Fyander for not washing her hands. "For Heaven's sake, pop thy hands under the pump, Deb! Upon my soul, if the London folk only knowed of thee and thy slovenly ways, they'd swaller their milk and butter more mincing than they do a'ready; and that's saying a good deal."'

[*Tess of the d'Urbervilles*, Thomas Hardy]

THE UDDER: HOW IT WORKS

The udder is both a factory and a warehouse. It is neatly divided into four compartments, each with its own teat. There is a much stronger barrier between left and right than between back and front but about 60% of the milk comes from the back two quarters.

Milk is synthesised in the *alveoli*. An alveolus is a minute balloon with a single layer of epithelial cells which continually secrete milk into the hollow of the alveolus (its *lumen*) where the milk is stored. The cow's bloodstream supplies the cells with milk constituents, and part of the blood's major route on its way back to the heart from the udder is the 'milk vein' you can see quite clearly running along the cow's abdominal wall. (There is no proof of the old belief that the bigger the milk vein, the greater the cow's yield.) Milk is secreted into the alveolar lumens at a constant rate for twelve hours after milking, then the rate gradually declines. When the pressure in the alveoli becomes excessive, secretion ceases.

Each alveolus has a capillary milk duct leading to a network of similar ducts which eventually channel into a few main milk ducts and discharge through a gland into the teat cistern. The milk finally finds its way out of the udder through the sphinctered teat canal.

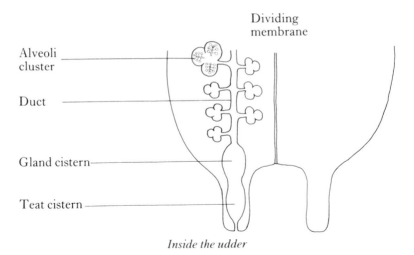

Inside the udder

Milk does not leak into the teats continuously. Its release has to be stimulated so that the relevant muscles can persuade the milk out of the alveoli, down the capillary milk ducts and into the teat cisterns where it waits for the pressure of a calf's sucking to draw it out. This process of release from the alveoli is known as *let-down* and is a crucial stage of milking. It is controlled by a hormone and is a conditioned reflex to a familiar stimulus associated with milking, be it the bunting of a calf, the washing and massaging of the udder, or any other preparatory routines which the cow habitually and clearly expects before being milked. Some cows are stimulated to let-down by the sound of concentrates rattling in their feeders, but beware of this becoming a habit: there are times when the cows will not receive concentrates at all and there are others when the feeding of concentrates is nothing to do with milking time.

The let-down signal may be visual, auditory, tactile, or a smell – all the senses come into it, and so does the time of day. Cows are essentially creatures of habit: best results come from milking them quietly at a regular time, in a wholly regular and predictable routine, with a clear indication to them that it *is* milking time, because without let-down you and the cow are in trouble. Any upset or change in routine is likely to disrupt the let-down reflex and if you try and milk with inadequate let-down you will get less out of her and could well damage the udder tissues. You will not get proper let-down if the cow is upset by noise, rough treatment, or anything out of the ordinary. Adrenalin can stop milk flow instantly and a cow must *want* to be milked or she will never let-down, despite the fact that modern dairy cows have been carefully selected over generations for ease of let-down as well as placidity in the parlour, healthy udders, good yields and milk quality.

Once let-down has been stimulated – and it usually proceeds within half a minute of the trigger – milking must be carried out promptly and fully. There is actually a time limit on the whole process from stimulation and let-down through milking to the cessation of milk flow, and for the sake of the cow and yourself you should attempt to work according to *her* timing. On average you have perhaps six to eight minutes from the start of let-down to the end of milking (it varies from cow to cow) and if you do not complete your task in that period you will not get another drop out of her during the session, however hard you try.

For about the first minute, the rate of milk flow increases to a maximum and is under quite a lot of pressure in the udder. The flow remains at a maximum rate for a short while and then declines rather fast. Cows are very individual and the rate at which milk can be removed from the udder depends not only on the rate of flow but also partly on habit and largely on the actual size of the teat canal. The bigger its diameter, the quicker you can extract the milk (and the easier it is for bacteria to enter too). Some cows are born to be slow milkers and there is nothing at all you can do about them or about their daughters – teat structure is heritable. Some cows can be milked out in less than three minutes, whatever their yield, and others may take more than seven minutes, however efficient you are.

Frequency of milking

Most people milk twice a day. It is not necessary to milk strictly at twelve-hour intervals, though yields might be a little more if you do so because of the twelve-hour secretion rate in the alveoli. It *is* important, however, that whatever time you choose to milk you do so at the *same* time every day, whether it is 7 a.m. and 7 p.m. or 4 a.m. and 2 p.m. A ratio of fourteen hours to ten hours is very reasonable.

Some large dairy farms milk three times a day to obtain increased profits and yields but the results are variable. No one has asked the cow what she feels about trudging into the parlour three times a day, reducing the time she can spend watching the meadow butterflies or exploring the hedges. The theory, however, is that the more often milk is extracted, the faster it is created.

On the other hand, the less often you milk the less milk she will produce, and some people only milk once a day, especially in the later stages of the lactation. The assumption in nature is that the milk is not wanted, so why waste energy in producing it? Some cows will dry themselves off quite quickly when put on once-a-day milking.

Again, the most important rule is a regular pattern of milking frequency: do not chop and change between once, twice or three times a day. A cow likes to know what her day will bring, and what right do you have to alter her comfortable habits at whim? No cow can trust an erratic human.

HOW TO MILK

Even if you intend to milk by machine, make a point of learning and practising hand-milking. It is only by hand-milking that you can really understand the udder and get to know the individual cow – and she you. It takes more time and patience but it can pay dividends.

Some cows, machine-milked all their lives, might object to hand-milking at first but most enjoy it, especially if the milker is relaxed and conversational. If you are a complete beginner, practise on someone else's cow until you are confident. Do not learn on your own first cow because it could ruin the start of a beautiful friendship! Ideally try your hand on an elderly cow who has acquired phlegmatism in her maturity. Choose a cow who is yielding perhaps 10 litres a day; if she is at a higher level you risk damaging her udder by your ineptitude, and if she is much lower you will find it harder to extract her milk anyway.

Dress for the occasion. You are going to be in very close contact with the cow: make sure that your hair will not tickle her and that your feet are well shod because cows can be clumsy at times and the weight of a cow whose hoof happens to be resting on your toe can be worse than uncomfortable. Cows are also easily upset by strangers and strange events, and their instant reaction is to lift their tails and urinate or dung – and the stuff splashes.

You need to be comfortable at your task. Squat on your haunches if your leg muscles are used to such a posture, or use a three-legged milking stool. A four-legged one is too cumbersome; a three-legged one can become a part of you and can be rotated smartly out of the way or to a new position.

Having tied the cow at the front end, and perhaps put a chain across behind her to keep her reasonably stationary, give her something to eat: it will keep her occupied and take her mind off your ham-fisted first efforts at milking. Let her know where you are all the time, with a comforting hand on her rump.

Now wash her udder with clean, hand-hot water and a disposable cloth. Be neither tentative nor aggressive in this, as in all other activities concerning cows. Udder washing serves several purposes. It gets rid of mud, dung and loose hair so that they will not fall into your pail of freshly drawn milk; it softens the teats a little to make milking easier for both of you; it massages the udder to stimulate let-down; and it gives you a chance to check her udder thoroughly for any signs of mastitis, small wounds or sore teats.

Experienced milkers tend to hold the milk-pail between their knees so that it can be swung out of harm's way if necessary. You will no doubt find it easier to put the bucket on the floor: you have enough to concentrate on in the early stages as it is.

Sit close up to the cow (customarily on her right) and press your head against her flank, partly to reassure her with physical contact and partly so that you can sense every move she is about to make. For example, if you feel her gathering her body together and perhaps edging her back feet forward and apart and hunching her back a little, watch out: she is about to urinate. If your hair tickles her, you deserve the automatic flick of her tail-switch across your ear – and if her tail is dirty it can be an unpleasant earful. The closer you sit against the cow, by the way, the less effective any kick will be, but very few cows kick out of spite.

Now for the skilled part. Your aim is to encourage milk out of the teat canal, then give it a brief chance to refill the cistern (something like a whisky dispenser) and then milk it out again. You need to apply a little pressure at the top of the teat to trap the milk in the cistern, and while maintaining that pressure you should gradually apply pressure down the length of the teat to ease the trapped milk down and out. This pressure is both a squeeze and a slight, gentle, downward draw – but remember you are dealing with a living udder: do not pinch or strangle the teat, or tug it off her udder. Force is not necessary. Just apply firm enough pressure to draw out the milk. The udder is precious and you should treat it with considerable respect. Restrict your squeezing to the actual teat: if you grip above it you will certainly damage the tissues.

Practise the milking 'grip' and squeeze on something inanimate before you go anywhere near a real cow. Grasp the practice teat in your fist. Apply pressure at the top with your thumb and first finger. Maintain the hold while you successively squeeze with second and third finger. It is an unnatural sequence at first (your hand wants to start with the little finger and work towards the index finger) but it will soon become quite automatic. Release the pressure at the end of the sequence so that the teat can fill up again. When you are actually milking the cow this release will only be momentary, especially once the session is well underway and the milk is flowing well. It is rather like riding a bicycle: once you have mastered it you cannot imagine that it was ever difficult, nor can you stop to think about exactly how you do it. Your hands will find milking hard work at first and they will probably ache with the effort for several milkings – and they will ache again, however experienced you are, if you recommence milking after a break of more than a few weeks.

Enough of practice sticks: back to the real live cow. You are on your stool, head against her flank, milk-pail in place, hands thoroughly scrubbed and the udder washed and massaged. Take one teat in each hand. Some people milk the back two together and then the front two together, especially when there's a difference in size between front and back. For example, Jerseys often have such small back teats that it is almost a finger-and-thumb job, whereas an elderly Longhorn might have four huge, long teats that you can hardly get your fist around or the bucket under and it makes no odds which two you milk together – fronts, backs, same sides, or kitty-corners if that is what you find easiest. But you should make a habit of milking two teats together for the sake of speed, and should also complete two teats before starting the other two. Milk the pair of teats alternately, first one handful then the other, and get a pleasant rhythm going. Sing along with it if you like: the cow might appreciate it.

Once you have stimulated let-down and started milking the cow, let nothing interrupt until both of you have finished the job. If you really despair as a beginner, hand over to an expert for the sake of the cow (who by that time will have decided to withhold her milk from all and sundry anyway) but if you relax, and if the cow is a sensible one, you will find that after what seems an eternity of unproductive manipulation a small trickle will begin to emerge and in no time at all it is purling into the pail and frothing the surface with each warm, powerful gush.

Do not be determined to pull out every last drop, even if the creamiest part is the last out of the udder. Once let-down is over, it is over and that is that, and you are putting unnecessary strain on the udder if you keep trying to milk it. If the cow holds back her milk, even if you are convinced that there is plenty more in there, let her be. It can always be milked out at the next session.

When you are experienced, milk quickly enough to keep pace with the cow. Once a teat is no longer full enough to be grasped comfortably in your fist, use finger and thumb for a few strokes to finish off the teat but go gently – don't yank it down like a piece of elastic, and massage the udder as you strip out the teat. If too much is left in the udder habitually, the cow comes to no harm but she will begin to reduce her daily yield and thus her overall yield for the current lactation. She will probably dry off much sooner too. Overstripping, however, can be damaging.

The milked-out udder hangs in soft folds – a very different receptacle to the plumped-up bag she came into the parlour with. Give the teats another wash to remove the last traces of milk then apply a teat dip to disinfect it. The teats are very vulnerable immediately after milking and they are wide open to bacteria. Use a proper dairy teat-dip solution, which effectively seals the ends of the teats and is usually iodine-based and therefore a deep brownish yellow that tints them a little. Put the solution in a teat-cup – any receptable of a convenient size to let each teat be dipped to its full extent in the liquid, one by one. Some people use sprays (a small plastic garden hand-spray is ideal) but dipping is more thorough, and breathing in iodine spray is good for neither man nor beast.

Make a habit of recording each cow's yield periodically. At least note yields mentally every day and actually record them weekly or monthly. Sudden changes in yield forewarn you of a problem or give you a clue that the cow is bulling.

THE MILKING ROUTINE: A CHECKLIST

Whether you milk by hand or by machine, the routines are basically as follows. Keep them simple and consistent.

1. Ensure that parlour, milker, equipment and cow are *clean*. The floor of the milking area should be scrubbable and scrubbed; the milker should have very clean hands and wear an overall and head-cover; the cow should have clean feet, tail and flanks, and clean udder and teats.
2. Start milking within a minute of stimulating let-down.
3. Squirt the first milk from each teat into a strip-cup to to check for signs of mastitic clotting or traces of blood.
4. Complete milking as quickly as possible and stop when the flow stops.
5. Apply a teat dip and make sure teats and udder are dry before the cow goes out.
6. Record individual yields.
7. Remove the milk from the milking area to a separate milk room immediately; cover it and cool it quickly.
8. Thoroughly wash out all milking equipment after each milking session, and use a dairy detergent and disinfectant.

MACHINE MILKING

Follow the manufacturer's recommendations about vacuum pressure (higher pressure gives faster extraction but increases the risk of damage to the teats), pulsation rate, machine maintenance and cleaning, and keep a constant check on the state of teat-cup liners – the part that is in contact with the living cow. Watch out for 'creeping' cups which find their way so high up the teat that they strangle it at the top (teats can literally turn white) or alternatively the 'drawing' cups which go on pulling down at dry, empty teats, either because the front teats milk out sooner than the back ones or because you left them on too long. Be aware of the front/back difference and make a point of helping the back quarters to catch up by massaging them.

Make absolutely certain that you never overmilk by machine. You can cause considerable internal damage to the udder tissues by leaving the cluster attached to the cow when her milk flow has finished. The trouble with any machine is that cows are individuals and they are also living creatures. Try putting your thumb into a pulsating teat-cup, then you will know how it feels to the cow.

THE DAIRY

Those who are contracted to sell their milk to the MMB are obliged to cool it promptly to below 5°C and to store it in a refrigerated farm bulk tank or vat. The milk is cooled inside the tank; the evening yield is maintained overnight at 4.5°C or less, and the morning yield is added immediately after milking and must be cooled to that same temperature within half an hour. The milk is collected later in the morning by the board's tanker and you can then wash out and sterilise the whole system, from teat cups to bulk tank, well before the afternoon milking session. Automatic cleaning systems can be set in motion by the tanker driver before he leaves the farm.

If you do not sell to the board, you would be well advised to cover, remove and cool freshly drawn milk immediately after milking just the same, having filtered it first if it is not already filtered in a pipeline system. However thoroughly you clean your cow, little specks of this and that always seem to find their way into the milk.

Hygiene in the milk-room or dairy is absolutely vital: *everything* must be thoroughly scrubbed and sterilised, and the cat and the collie should be banned. Rinse everything immediately after use with cold water first, then sterilise with lots of boiling water or approved dairy chemicals, and always air-dry utensils rather than use drying cloths.

There are many things you can do with the milk, apart from feeding it just as it is to calves or to your family, and if you heat-treat it in some way to kill bacteria and extend its keeping qualities you will need special equipment. Your ADAS dairy husbandry adviser will give you plenty of ideas, information and literature on different ways of treating and processing milk.

Untreated milk

Untreated milk is 'raw' milk – bottled or cartoned without being heat-treated in any way. Produced cleanly, it will keep fresh for a few days in the fridge and it is incomparable for flavour and for vitamin content, with all the natural enzymes unimpaired.

Heat-treated milk

Pasteurisation kills pathogenic organisms in milk but in theory does not affect its palatability or nutritional value; in practice it damages the protein content and probably reduces at least the vitamin C. It should keep for up to five days in the fridge. There are two methods of pasteurisation. Either heat the milk to 63–66°C and maintain at that temperature for half an hour, then cool immediately to 10°C or less; or heat the milk to at least 72°C for at least fifteen seconds, then cool rapidly to 10°C or less (this is the HTST process – high temperature short time).

Cream

Cream contains everything that whole milk does but in different proportions, the most obvious difference being the greater concentration of butterfat. On the whole the higher the fat content, the thicker the cream, but thickness can also be controlled by manufacturing processes.

The simplest way of separating cow's milk is by leaving fresh whole milk to stand. The fat globules are lighter than the other milk components; they therefore rise to the surface and congregate. The rise is slow: an average fat globule (say 3 micrometres in diameter) will rise 0.6mm in one hour. Bigger ones rise faster and clusters of globules faster still, but speed is relative and the whole process is gentle and slow. The age-old practice is to set the evening milk overnight in broad, shallow containers and then skim off the risen cream in the morning. You can use a perforated skimmer or 'float', which catches the cream and drains off any underlying milk, or you can simply use a large spoon or a thin saucer. It is not particularly efficient; you are bound to leave quite a lot of the cream behind, but why be greedy? You can also buy special pans which let you drain away the skimmed milk, leaving the cream sticking to the pan.

The more efficient method for those who are dealing with any quantity of milk and who are selling their cream, or for those whose cows produce very small fat globules which tend to homogenise rather than separate, is to make use of centrifugal force. Centrifugal cream separators can be electrically operated or hand-turned and can be adjusted to give creams with different butterfat contents.

The individual globule is in for a shock: it will be separated 6,500 times faster by a centrifugal machine than by a setting pan. Separation is easier if the milk is warm (50°C) because it is then less viscous than when it is cold, so it is sensible to use the machine soon after milking.

If you are serious about selling cream, try and find an all stainless-steel separator for the sake of hygiene. New, smaller separators (up to about 450 litres an hour) tend to have corrodible parts and it might be worth locating a reconditioned stainless-steel model instead. Be careful about the type of disinfectant you use on any aluminium alloy equipment.

Cream for sale is described according to fat content, texture and heat treatment (if any). The minimum milk-fat contents are as follows:

Clotted	55%
Double	48%
Whipping	35%
Single	18%
Half cream	12%

Farm cream is not a regulated description and in fact farm cream is often the richest of all.

Clotted cream will keep for up to ten days in the fridge. Let the cream set in large, shallow pans (traditionally holding about 10 litres of milk) for twelve to twenty-four hours. Then heat the whole lot (milk and all) in the same pan very slowly over a low heat to about 82–85°C and maintain that temperature for about threequarters of an hour. The surface of the cream will wrinkle. Cool slowly overnight, then skim off the thick yellow cream crust with a perforated ladle. Eight or nine litres of Channel Island milk might produce about half a kilogram of clotted cream.

Soured cream Pasteurised, homogenised single cream is soured commercially by adding a starter culture which converts lactose into lactic acid. A dash of rennet (the milk-clotting enzyme in a calf's stomach) will thicken the cream. To sour untreated cream, just leave it out of the fridge for a few days, or add some lemon juice for instant souring.

Skimmed Milk

Today an increasingly health-conscious public is beginning to reject cream in favour of its unfatty residue: skimmed milk. Skim is still a highly nutritious food; it has higher calcium levels than whole milk and retains its protein but it does lose most of the fat-soluble vitamins A and D. However, if that is what people want, that is what you would do well to give them and it is almost easier to find a market for skimmed milk than for cream. Sales of low-fat milk already account for about 15% of the liquid milk market and are expected to double in five years. Your own marketing could, of course, emphasise the 'health' value of your product, especially if your own cows can fairly claim to be additive-free and contented.

The regulations stipulate that skimmed milk must not contain more than 0.3% fat and semi-skimmed 1.5–1.8%. The milk must be heat-treated and properly labelled. To make sense of a skimmed-milk enterprise, you must also find a profitable outlet for the cream. Double and whipping are the most popular (especially if you can supply local restaurants, bakers etc.). Single cream tends to separate out unless you can afford a homogeniser. If you own a pasteuriser, the major capital expenditure has already been made (pasteuriser, refrigeration, extra dairy space, bottling equipment and washing equipment) and the separator will be a comparatively minor extra, but it is a different story if you are starting from scratch.

Ice-cream

Ice-cream could be a major enterprise for those with a small dairy herd. There is an increasing demand for pure foods with interesting tastes and textures and there is ample scope for personal flair in devising flavours and marketing the product. Ice-cream is a good way to get round quotas; the situation may change but at present the regulations refer only to milk, cream, butter and cheese, so if you have no quota at all you could simply turn all your milk into ice-cream, or if you do have a quota and are likely to exceed it you can turn surplus milk into ice-cream. Because it can be stored in the freezer, you can make it in the months when your milk production would otherwise be over quota and then sell it when the season is right.

In theory it is possible to convert excess milk into ice-cream and sell it wholesale for at least double the cost of the ingredients – usually substantially more – and the economics of ice-cream are attractive, especially if combined with farm yogurt-making and as long as you have a professional attitude and have researched the local market thoroughly. You will need a local authority licence to manufacture ice-cream for sale – or rather your premises will require such a licence and will be inspected regularly. It is quite possible that in some areas you will need planning permission as well: check with the council in the early stages.

To understand the principles, first try making ice-cream by hand in the kitchen for the family, using any good cookery-book recipe. Once you have worked out that ice-cream on a larger scale is a good-looking enterprise in your circumstances, then you can think about commercial equipment. Be prepared to be shocked at the prices (see Appendix) but there is a good market in secondhand equipment which is advertised occasionally in the farming press and more regularly in the ice-cream makers' trade journals. The Ice Cream Alliance is the one for smaller producers, and their journal is worth reading just for the delightful headings in the 'Buyer's Guide' – ripple sauces, slush freezers, stickless novelties, tricycles, nibbed nuts, mango pulp . . .

Commercial ice-cream making is a simple basic process. Very broadly, you mix raw milk, cream, sugar, flavouring, eggs (optional) and skimmed-milk powder and put them all into a vat, heat to the temperature required by the local authority for pasteurisation (they will be strict about the use of recording thermometers to prove that the right temperature was achieved and maintained) and then freeze it, with agitation. The bulk of the ingredients come from your cows: a 100–litre mix, for example, would probably contain 65 litres of milk plus 16kg of double cream (made from about 225 litres of whole milk). Dairy ice-cream must contain at least 5% milk fat.

Now you can add air. No, it is not a cheat: air makes the ice-cream softer, which many people prefer because of its texture and because it is less of a shock to tongues and teeth. Fifty per cent added air is average and, as ice-cream is sold by volume rather than by weight, your 100–litre mix could become at least 150 litres of ice-cream.

It is perfectly possible to sell good dairy ice-cream for perhaps £2 a litre, if you have built up a good reputation, and it will not take you long to work out the high level of possible returns compared to selling milk to the MMB. You still have the skimmed milk left over from making the double cream and you could turn that into yogurt for extra revenue.

Talk to your ADAS milk products adviser for a thorough and realistic assessment of your true potential and for advice on the equipment you will need – most of it stainless-steel and expensive – and where you can buy it secondhand. Of course, if everybody jumps on the ice-cream float it will soon melt. (Don't forget to insure the storage freezer and all its contents.)

Yogurt

Yogurt can be made from whole or skimmed milk. There must be absolutely no trace of antibiotics because they will kill off the lactic acid bacteria you need to culture the milk.

Yogurt is expected to contain at least 8.5% milk solids-not-fat and 3% milk protein. Low-fat yogurts should contain 0.5–2.0% fat, or less than 0.5% if described as 'very low-fat' or 'skimmed milk' yogurt.

The secrets of yogurt making are well covered in the dairying books listed in the Bibliography. Basically, you heat the milk to just below boiling point, cool to hand-hot, mix in some starter, keep it warm and sealed for a while to incubate, let it cool to restrict further production of lactic acid by the bacteria once a curd has formed, then refrigerate.

Starter culture can be purchased as such or you can begin with some ready-made yogurt from the shops. Incubation can be in a simple haybox, a thermos flask (for small quantities) or an electrically heated yogurt cabinet.

Yogurt is usually sold in 5oz pots (four to the pint) and you could probably charge 20p a pot. Be careful about quotas: if you make yogurt from skimmed milk left over after making cream for ice-cream, you have not sold any cream as cream and you are probably safely outside quota rules, but if you use skim left over after making cream sold as *cream*, quota regulations will probably apply.

Butter

Butter is usually made from cream with a 35–40% butterfat content and it takes about 20 litres of milk to produce a kilogram of butter. The basic principle is to agitate either fresh or ripe cream so that the fat globules come together in grains, then pour off the liquid (buttermilk), rinse the grains thoroughly in cold water several times, and work them into a homogenous mass, expelling every trace of liquid and adding salt if required.

Sounds easy; and sometimes it is. The South American cowboys simply attached jars of milk to their saddles, spent the day riding the prairies to chase their herds, and by the time they camped their jars were full of butter. Children like to experiment by shaking a bottle partly filled with milk but it takes a very long time to turn it into butter. It is easier if you use a churn of some kind – a 'Blow' churn (big glass container with paddles acting like egg-beaters and turned manually), or an end-over churn (heavy wooden utensils that are turned over and over and over again), or an ingenious kind of dog-driven churn with a treadmill, or an electric mixer. The smallholder suppliers' catalogues are full of all kinds of churns, driven by hand or by electricity, in glass or wood, with prices ranging very widely from perhaps £25 or £30 for a Blow churn to £600 for an electrically driven wooden work of art.

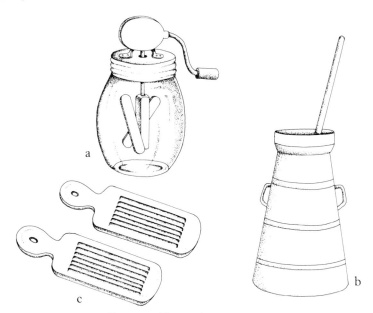

Butter-making equipment:
(a) Hand-paddled 'Blow' churn
(b) Old-fashioned plunger churn
(c) Scotch hands

Buttermilk

Buttermilk is delicious to drink. All it has lost is the butterfat and vitamin A, and it can be used in place of skimmed milk to make curds for cheesecake or crowdie.

Cheese

Cheese-making is a classic example of human determination to turn disaster into victory and to create something good out of something bad.

In Britain the climate is kind to milk and we habitually drink it fresh. In many parts of the world, however, the climate rapidly turns milk sour and indeed in such areas people find fresh milk distasteful: they prefer it sour. Even in Britain, of course, fresh milk cannot remain that way for long without treatment, nor would it have been available during the winter months not so long ago because there simply was not enough winter fodder to keep the milk flowing. So there had to be ways of preserving milk for long periods by exploiting its tendency to sour.

Some say that the first cheese was made by mistake. Nomadic tribesmen in the Arabian deserts four thousand years ago carried their milk in pouches made from the stomachs of sheep and goats. After a day of being bounced around in the sunshine as the tribesmen travelled across the sands, the milk reacted with the natural rennin in the ruminant pouches and became curds and whey, the basis of all cheeses.

Rennin is the enzyme in a calf's stomach which clots the milk so that the digestive processes have something to work on. Rennet is an agent containing rennin and pepsin and it is used today by cheese-makers to coagulate the curds. You can also buy 'vegetarian' rennet, which is derived from fungi rather than from calves, but it tends to make a more bitter cheese.

Cheese-makers also use starters, which are bacterial cultures that activate the making of lactic acid from the milk's natural sugar (lactose), turning it sour. Different organisms act at different rates and produce different levels of acidity in given times, and part of the art of cheese-making is to choose the right organisms and incubate them at the best temperature for the ideal length of time to achieve the required pH levels. Starters can be bought in liquid or freeze-dried form.

All cheeses depend on the quality of the milk: you can only make the best cheese if you know what the cows have eaten and that they are free of disease and well cared for. Some people claim that the best cheeses are made from raw rather than pasteurised milk, and with your own cows you have the opportunity of finding out whether this is true.

Cheese-making is an art and its intricacies are beyond the scope of this book but here is some basic information.

Soft cheeses. The simplest cheeses are the soft ones: they ripen quickly, remain moist, and will keep only for a few days. For cottage cheese, warm ½ litre of milk in a saucepan to 38°C; transfer to a pudding basin and add the juice of half a lemon (or a teaspoon of vinegar), then leave for quarter of an hour. The acid sours the milk quickly and you soon have curds and whey. Strain them through a muslin bag and let it drip for perhaps a day. You could add a little rennet to speed up the souring process.

Cream cheese is equally simple to make for home use. Set raw cream in the usual way and put it aside to ripen, then simply bag and drain it. Or boil fresh cream then add it to milk fresh from the cow and let it cool to body temperature. Add rennet; then strain the curds when they have set, and leave to ripen. Commercial cream cheese, like commercial cottage cheese, needs a starter culture.

Hard Cheese. The more whey you remove from the curds, the harder the cheese and the longer it will keep. Mix last night's milk with the fresh morning yield, heat to about 30°C, add starter to sour the milk and ten minutes later add some rennet to clot it into a firm junket. Keep it warm to incubate the starter until you reach the right level of acidity, then cut the curd into small pieces and scald and drain it to release the whey. The pieces will begin to fuse together: chop into large blocks and 'cheddar' by methodically turning and piling the chunks to create a cheddary texture. Chop up the blocks into small pieces again, add salt (for preservation and flavour) then pack into muslin-lined moulds for pressing. This expels more whey and lets the curds knit together. Next day, wash the cheese in warm water, press again for a short while, and then dress in swathes of fine cheese-cloth dipped in melted lard. Press again and then store the cheese to mature it, turning it regularly.

The making of hard cheese does need some equipment and there are lots of smallholder suppliers who can help. You can devise your own presses and moulds, but even for small home cheeses you need to invest in a good dairy thermometer and an acidimeter. The acidity of the cheese at various stages is vital and varies according not only to the cheese but also to where you make it. Adjusting to local conditions is part of the art and satisfaction of cheese-making.

Whey

Whey is the watery, greenish-yellow liquid left from cheese-making and it is full of milk solids, especially lactose. When hard cheese is made, about 85–90% of the milk used becomes whey. It used to be considered a waste product, fit only for pigs or as a field fertiliser at best, but it is now recognised as a useful source of high-quality protein which can be turned into special products like whey butter and cheese or used as an ingredient in manufactured food like ice-cream, confectionery, soft drinks, margarines, baked goods and meat products. It can even be turned into alcohol. How about that for an enterprise? In Russia they produce a sparkling whey beer, in the United States a whey wine, and elsewhere whey is turned into fuel in the form of methane and ethanol.

That is the joy of dairying. With a little imagination and flair you can work miracles and even make a good living.

X

OTHER OUTLETS

Keeping cows does not need to end with milk and there are many enterprises which could incorporate the sale of your dairy produce. You could sell clotted cream by post, or have a farm shop, for example, or sell cream teas at your own farm park. There are countless ways of luring the paying public to your holding, or of taking your produce and livestock out to the public for sale and display.

Then there are the by-products, like whey and manure, which can be exploited. Or perhaps you have a philanthropic streak and would like to educate children and adults about livestock, farming and the countryside either on your own farm or by setting up a special centre. Maybe you want to express certain philosophies through your holding – organic farming, silvopastoral farming, conservation, 'real' food etc. – or offer gourmet products to specialist markets that no one else has even imagined, let alone exploited. Or perhaps you have cows purely for the pleasure of their company, because you like them, or for the sake of sharing them with the local community.

'Alternative' enterprises are fashionable among land-owners, large and small, but very few publications on the subject bother to mention cows at all: it is assumed that the role of the cow is already exploited to a maximum. That is a false assumption (use your imagination) and anyway there is plenty of scope for keeping cows without 'exploiting' them (such a greedy word) but still without turning your holding into a charity rest-home for cows. (Though why not? Working horses have rest-homes. Cows work as hard or harder than other domestic animals. Don't they deserve holidays and retirement homes too?)

The aim of this chapter is to set off a few trains of thought rather than to give detailed guidance on how to make a success of specific cow-based enterprises. Make yourself comfortable, open your mind, start reading, and dream a little. (You can carry on dreaming when you've got your head pressed into the cow's comforting flank at milking time.) But let's start with the more obvious and practical outlets for cows.

Cows for the Smallholder

DAIRY HEIFERS

You can probably make a fair enterprise by entering into a contract rearing scheme with a nearby dairy farm. The two usual systems are:

1. The breeder sells calves to the rearer, who takes full responsibility for transport, expenses and losses. The original breeder has first option to buy back the heifers at an agreed price eight weeks before calving.
2. The breeder retains ownership of the heifers and is charged for the rearer's expenses, though the rearer pays for transport, veterinary and medicinal expenses and any losses.

BEEF

Beef cattle make good use of surplus food and grazing, if you have such surpluses, and their demands are nothing like as exacting as those of dairy cows. They do not require highly skilled labour once they are past the weaning hurdle, and they can keep your land fertile by converting straw into manure. However, they do tie up capital. Even a very young calf could cost you £100 (more for Continental-breed steers) and veterinary and feeding costs could be high up to the weaning stage. Housing, too, can be a drain on your resources if you choose an enterprise that depends on it.

Markets can be fickle and should be carefully studied well in advance so that you know exactly what kind of animal and what degree of finish does best where. It is the same with any enterprise, and a vital point too often overlooked: *know* your market *before* you begin your enterprise, and then aim for the market and *sell* to it – actively. Don't just raise a few cattle and sell them when you run out of space or grass, or enthusiasm. When planning the grazing, do remember that the cattle are *growing*: they will be bigger at the end of the season and will therefore need greater areas of grazing per head, especially as the value of the grass is decreasing fast. Plan the enterprise right the way through: buy right, manage right and sell right.

The major markets for beef animals are:

1. Autumn-born suckler calves sold to graziers in spring.
2. Spring-born suckler calves sold in autumn for in-wintering.
3. Store cattle.
4. Fat cattle.

Suckled calves, especially on their own mothers, have a head start over all other beef animals. The aim is to minimise any check in progress at the weaning stage, and good management at this crucial time really puts a bloom on the calf if you want to sell it post-weaning.

Fig. xxiii THE BEEF INDUSTRY

CALF REARING Buy in at 4–10 days old (very vulnerable) Sell at 12–14 weeks old
INTENSIVE BEEF Housed for entire period and intensively fed   (e.g. barley beef) Usually Friesian males (often entire) Finished at 10–14 months, 400–450kg

SEMI-INTENSIVE BEEF
(a) *15 MONTH GRASS/CEREAL*
  Born winter/early spring (late maturing breeds)
  Weaned at 5 weeks
  Grazed on good pasture first summer
  Fattened on concentrates
  Finished at 13–17 months, 400–450kg
 	
(b) *18 MONTH GRASS/CEREAL*
  Born summer or autumn, weaned at 5 weeks
  Grazed the following season
  Yard finished on silage and barley
  Slaughtered at 15–20 months, 400–520kg
 	
(c) *20–24 MONTH GRASS SILAGE*
  Born October–April (early maturing types, often heifers)
  Spring calves store-fed first winter (silage/hay), fattened on good
    grazing second season
  Winter calves store-grazed first season, silage/hay and concentrates in
    yard, then finished on grass in second season with supplementary
    feeding if needed
  Slaughtered at 20–24 months, 430–530kg

EXTENSIVE Two full grazing seasons – finish in yard or on grass depending on season   of birth and markets. Finish at 24 months or more. Heavy carcase.

SUCKLER BEEF
Extensive. Calve autumn to early spring. Cows utilise hill and upland
  grazing, inaccessible lowland grass, arable by-products and grass break
  crops. Late weaning to give youngstock maximum growth period on milk.

Store cattle are the simplest of all. They are maintained on rather low feeding (quality and/or quantity) and their rate of growth is greatly reduced. That is why they are called stores: they are not really expected to make any progress. However, they catch up with other animals once they are restored to full feeding levels – a phenomenon known as compensatory

Cows for the Smallholder

Fig xxiv BEEF TARGETS

BARLEY BEEF	*Bulls*	*Steers*
Weight gains per day:		
0–5 weeks	0.45kg	0.45kg
6–12 weeks	1.0kg	0.9kg
3–6 months	1.3kg	1.2kg
6 months to slaughter	1.4kg	1.3kg
Age at slaughter	338 days	345 days
Weight at slaughter	445kg	404kg
Carcase weight	231kg	211kg
15 MONTH GRASS/CEREAL BEEF	*Winter calf*	*Spring calf*
Weight gains per day:		
Birth to turn-out	0.7kg	0.7kg
Grazing	0.7kg	0.6kg
Winter finishing	1.1kg	1.2kg
18 MONTH GRASS/CEREAL BEEF		
Weight gains per day:		
Birth to turn-out		0.75kg
Grazing		0.8–0.9kg
Winter finishing		0.8–0.9kg
20–24 MONTH GRASS BEEF		
Weight gains per day:		
Birth to turn-out		0.7kg
First summer grazing		0.7kg
Store winter		0.5kg
Second summer		1.0kg

growth – and you can exploit this if you want to reduce winter feeding costs and then make full use of spring and summer grazing.

Barley beef animals, intensively reared, are usually sold early at perhaps twelve or fourteen months old and their diet of cereals with only limited hay or straw gives them a lean, sleek finish at probably 400–450kg liveweight. They do need some animal protein in the rations as well, perhaps some fishmeal.

Fat cattle can be sold to liveweight outlets like the weekly local cattle auctions ('on the hoof') or to slaughterers who base their prices on deadweights ('on the hook'). Research your market carefully: a supermarket's requirements are very different to those of a local hotel, and a pie-maker's needs are not the same as those of a nouvel cuisine chef.

'Fat' cattle are not fat but ready for slaughter, that is, 'finished'. A well-finished beef animal has achieved a marketable weight but that does not necessarily mean maximum size. It is the proportion and distribution of saleable meat that counts. The ideal carcase is usually lean, with just enough fat to help the cook but not so much that it is classed as waste trim. The loin flesh of the living animal should feel firm, not fatty and soft.

All cows, even the high-class dairy cow, will probably end up as meat but a cow's potential carcase rapidly becomes less valuable for beef after her third calving and if she is a specialist dairy breed, like the Jersey, her meat will be spurned by the consumer unless it is disguised in pies or sausages. Old cows of any breed tend to produce tough, dry meat and dairy females also tend to have too much fat in the carcase (fat is necessary to the dairy cow as a means of storing energy reserves against the demands of a suckling calf or a milking machine). The majority of beef animals are steers – castrated males; steers grow faster than heifers but heifers of early-maturing breeds put on fat at a younger age than their breed brothers and are therefore slaughtered younger and lighter.

Entire bulls grow faster than steers and do not need growth promoters implanted in them (castration deprives steers of an important source of growth hormones). They have more efficient food conversion rates but as a bull matures his neck and shoulder muscles develop and more of the carcase weight is thrown forward rather than being in the expensive back-end meat cuts.

DRAUGHT OXEN

Draught animals work perhaps as much as 80% of the world's cultivated land, and many more of them are used for road haulage. Draught oxen used to be a major source of farm power in this country and today some people are turning to them again. Their pace may be slower than tractors but they are not burning up irreplaceable and expensive fossil fuels, nor are they creating tyre pans or taking up valuable hours in the repair shed. Developments in technology in recent years have enormously improved the equipment and techniques used in draughtwork and it is no longer a primitive form of agriculture.

For the true husbander there is something enormously satisfying about managing an energy cycle within the holding. Cattle give manure to the land to compensate for the energy they take from it by grazing; grazing gives the cattle energy to produce exportable milk and meat, and also muscle power to draw a plough and other equipment to work the land, so that crops can be grown which can be sold and which feed the cattle, which . . . and so on.

Only cattle can give produce *and* power in this way. Heavy horses are fine animals but they only give you power and manure; sheep and goats give you manure and produce but not power (though they might be persuaded to draw a light cart); pigs are intelligent and can be trained to draughtwork but they lack the bulk and strength of cattle. A hefty, triple-purpose ox gives so much more.

It is quite feasible to use a milking cow as a draught animal as long as you do not ask too much of her and feed her according to the extra energy she is expending. However, it is more common to use oxen (steers) who, being deprived of their sexual drive, are placid and amenable beasts. They also have more weight and better muscling for effective draughtwork than your housecow. You might try a more exotic species altogether, like water buffalo or yak, but they are not really happy in our climate, though water buffalo are farmed in southern Europe and have been tried in France, Germany and England.

Experiments are being carried out in several parts of this country by institutions and by private individuals. In the early stages, handle young draught animals regularly and often so that they remain tame and come readily when called. Halter-train them from calfhood and, later, yoke them together for an hour or so a day. Then give them an old tyre or something to draw, and gradually work up the training, ensuring at each stage that they are content with their lot and are never asked to do something that unsettles them or that they have difficulty in achieving. Once a new lesson has been accepted, oxen never forget it and there is no need to repeat it. Train at a gentle pace: there is no advantage at all in trying to hurry and chivvy any bovine animal.

You can ride cattle, if you insist, but if you try it bareback you might find the bovine spine unbearably bony. Nor does the animal's shape and looseness of hide lend itself readily to being saddled. The gait takes getting used to (and don't ask them to do more than amble) and you need a halter rather than a bit and bridle for rein control, though simple bits have been devised by enthusiasts. Horns can be useful for attaching guide ropes.

MANURE

Cow manure is a precious gift indeed if you take care to rot it well before using it on the land and to store it properly in the meantime. Pile up soiled bedding in a heap to cook: aim to create warm, moist (but not waterlogged) conditions.

Cattle urine is rich in potash and nitrogen; its nitrogen content is easily extracted, which means almost instant fertilisation but also means that it can be lost quickly. Dung, on the other hand, is rich in phosphoric acid as well as nitrogen, and its nitrogen is released far more slowly. In principle a tonne of farmyard manure (dung, urine and bedding) contains about 5.5kg nitrogen, 2.3kg phosphoric acid and 5.5.kg potash, but much of the goodness is locked up and released only slowly, or is dissipated before the manure gets anywhere near a plant that can use it.

Bedding absorbs urine and therefore retains its nitrogen and potash. A tonne of straw can probably absorb enough urine and dung to form 4–6 tonnes of fresh manure; other types of bedding may have better absorption rates but are slower to decompose and not so good for improving the texture of the land. Copious straw bedding will absorb more urine and fix its nitrogen content but the resulting manure will only yield that nitrogen slowly to the plants.

The excretions of young animals contain less nitrogen and minerals because they extract the elements from their food with great efficiency in order to build up bone and muscle. When a beef animal has been fattened to the stage that its liveweight gains are almost entirely fat, its manure is much richer in nutrients. Cow manure is rather watery and decomposes very slowly; cows use a lot of the nitrogen and minerals in their food for making milk and developing the unborn calf, so their manure is less rich than that of fattening bullocks.

Cattle manure in general is 'cold': it is slow to ferment compared to 'hot' horse manure, which ferments rapidly and does not last long. Fresh manure is not good for crops and its texture (especially on straw bedding) makes field application difficult. It is often produced at a time of year when spreading is impracticable and therefore it is stored. Inevitably much of its goodness can be lost, especially the urine nitrogen.

The practice of letting bedding mount up *in situ* over a period, with fresh litter being added daily to give the animals a dry lying surface, is as good a way as any of excluding air from the potential manure and keeping it moist and heated. The same principles apply to manure stacks. The quality of manure is affected by the animals' diet to some extent, and also by losses in storage due to dilution, gaseous losses and leaching. Rainwater obviously dilutes, and helps to wash out nutrients (in an open, uncovered stack you can lose up to 20% of the nitrogen, 10% of the potash and as much as 35% of the phosphoric acid from leaching). Loosely stacked farmyard manure, too full of air and not generating enough heat, can lead to up to 40% of nitrogen being lost as ammonia – and as much as 10% on average in a better-packed stack. The effects can be cumulative and the longer the material is stored out of doors the more its manurial value is reduced. The flatter the heap, the greater the potential for loss. The dungstead should be a walled enclosure with a moisture-retaining floor under a roof for best conditions. Allow 1.0–1.4 cubic metres for every tonne of straw-based manure; or, to estimate what you have already, work on the basis of 700–1,000kg per cubic metre.

To make a good garden compost from farmyard manure, stack the manure on soil dusted with lime in 10cm layers with a sprinkling of soil between each layer. If it is more slurry than solid, add peat or leafmould.

Cover with a rain-shedding tarpaulin or an old piece of corrugated iron suspended at least a handsbreadth above the heap. In three or four months it will turn into a sweet, earthy, friable mould.

METHANE

Five years ago, scientists in Australia and the United States noted that levels of methane gas in the atmosphere were rapidly increasing and contributing to the 'greenhouse effect' that might ultimately lead to a melting of the polar ice-caps and thence to a substantial rise in sea-levels all over the world. There are four major sources of methane production: coal-mines, swamps, rice fields and ruminants. The scientists noted that the world's cattle population had doubled in the last fifty years and they connected this fact with the significant increase in atmospheric methane.

The Cistercian monks of Bethlehem Abbey have turned this problem into an advantage. They run a herd of 300 beef cattle and they have installed a 200,000–litre digestor which converts slurry into methane gas. The manure is recycled on their organic farm, and the gas is used to provide all the heating required by the monastery and farm.

The late Neil Wates, philosopher and practical farmer, put a lot of research into extracting and using methane produced by cattle, and others have also been investigating the possibilities. If the idea of making the most of your herd's 'waste' by-products is inspiring, contact one of the alternative technology groups listed in the Appendix.

GOING PUBLIC

This is a bold step and will only succed if your holding is well situated, your local planning authority is helpful, your neighbours are encouraging, you have a flair for marketing, you like people and can be diplomatic with all types, you have moral support at home, your bank manager is as far-sighted as you are, your research is very thorough, and luck is on your side.

The moment you open your doors to the public, your responsibilities multiply alarmingly. First and foremost, consider your cows and protect them from stress or actual physical harm, witting or unwitting, by the public. For example, keep a very sharp eye out for lethal litter, peculiar titbits, teasing and so on. Most cows accept and often enjoy milling throngs but some do not and certainly a calving cow should be given plenty of peace and privacy. Consider the public, too: you are responsible for their health and safety on your farm and must protect them from their own ignorance of the ways of cattle.

The planning authorities become involved the moment your enterprise is no longer purely agricultural and even earlier if it puts too many people on narrow country lanes. Ideally, invite a planning officer to the farm on an informal basis while you are still thinking about the kind of enterprise you want, and listen very carefully to his opinions and ideas. Talk to CoSIRA too (Council for Small Industries in Rural Areas). The main possibilities involving your cows are probably these, or any combination of them:

Farm shop selling your own cream, yogurt, ice-cream, cheeses, plain and flavoured milk (by licence). You might consider gourmet foods like clotted cream, smoked meats, pies, deep-freeze meat etc. either for sale on the premises or by mail order. You must put plenty of research into packaging, catalogues, pricing, promotion, and distribution systems. Talk to Dairy Crest Foods (see Appendix) about ideas they have discarded for mass production which might be ideal for small-scale on-farm produce.

Rare-breeds centre displaying rare breeds, giving lots of information about them and encouraging people to take an interest in the heritage and conservation aspects. *Please* display good specimens of the breed, very well looked after, and in attractive surroundings – not just a few scraggy old cows knee-deep in mud. You should be promoting animal welfare and husbandry as well as rare breeds.

Farm park with farm trails and tractor or cart rides to see cattle in the field, cows actually being milked, perhaps a lecture tour of the dairy too; small and intimate, or large scale. Draught oxen might have a role to play. You could have a theme park, perhaps based on a historic period with breeds and farming techniques to match: Longhorns, old-fashioned hay-making, hand-milking. For the ambitious, go back to the Dark Ages or beyond. Farm museums might be interesting, with examples of wooden butter churns and other paraphernalia, preferably in use, or dairying bygones for sale – you can do a roaring trade with pubs and Americans. An inspired packager will dream up appropriately presented dairy produce to sell to museum visitors. If you are rich, how about a Victorian dairy like the genuine octagonal beauty at Easton Farm Park in Suffolk with its decorative tiles, stained-glass windows and a fountain not just for decoration but to keep the room dairy-cool? Let your imagination run riot!

Farm school – something like the excellent Yarner Farm School on Dartmoor, where inner-city children spend a couple of weeks learning about farming both in theory and in practice – plenty of hands-on experience and a chance to relate to real live cattle for children who hardly ever see grass, let alone animals. There is also considerable scope for running short courses for adults – perhaps potential smallholders who want to learn before they decide to go ahead with their own enterprises. If your cows are patient, the amateurs can practise their hand-milking before they crucify their own animals.

Institutional farm, where children and adults can look after the cows and calves (but don't forget the holidays if it is a school). Some can get satisfaction from actually caring for the cattle; others (e.g. nursing homes) will get pleasure from just seeing them around, and perhaps some of the residents can turn their hand to dairy work if not to actual milking or bottle-feeding. But do not overlook the welfare of the cows in your desire to make life better for the institutionalised.

Cow care for owners going on holiday or into hospital or just desperate for a day off from milking. Offer a service of relief milking, emergency help, taking over a milk-round; it is often better to pay for a reliable service than to depend on friendly neighbours who always have a reason for being unavailable at the wrong moment. It will not be practical to open your own holding to temporary cows – you'll be importing disease, you could have problems with movement permits and transport, and anyway for cows home is best – so your service will have to be a mobile one: you go to the cows. Reliability is absolutely essential, of course, and you should also check your legal liabilities: what happens if a cow is stolen while under your care, or goes on the rampage in the next-door garden? It is a nice way of looking after cows if you do not have space for your own and you miss them.

MMB recording as a part-time employment – you can take on just one herd or several. It entails early rising once a month for each herd (you attend two consecutive milkings). Your job is to take milk samples, note each cow's yield, and fill in a lot of forms with details of calvings, services etc. It is a good way of setting up contacts and learning a lot about how other people manage their cows, and there is plenty of time to ask questions if the milker is in a reasonable mood.

Showing requires considerable dedication and money. It is a world of its own which is generally friendly to humble newcomers who are keen to learn. You will need cow-sized transport (co-ownership with friends?). Go to lots of shows first to find out what it is all about: talk to exhibitors, watch their preparations and their show-ring technique; talk to judges to see what they look for; see as many good examples of your own breed as possible to get your eye in for the good points.

Co-operative markets might be an idea in the right area – join with other local small-scale producers to offer a variety of goods at weekly public markets, either a stall in organised market places or set up your own market on the farm. Co-operation can extend to relief milking and pooling of equipment.

PAPER FARMING

It is a fact of farming life today that the desk work takes up almost as much time as the land and the livestock, to the resentment of those who prefer soil and oil on their hands rather than ink. The main reasons for this depressing increase in paper farming are the demands of bureaucracy, book balancers and agribusinessmen. You can reduce your paper mountain, but you will never escape it (the Ministry will make sure of that) and the well-managed mountain can be the key to the well-managed farm.

Though loth to add to the heap, I have to advocate record-keeping on the holding whether you have one housecow or a large herd. Records help you to see patterns – patterns which reflect your management practices. If you keep and *analyse* records regularly, you will soon see where you are going wrong. Combine that with an eye for the well-being of your livestock and your land, and you will benefit them and yourself. The art of record-keeping is to accumulate details in such a way that you can identify and extract the pattern easily and then use your flair and judgment, based on personal experience, to take action according to your circumstances.

If you want to compare your enterprise's performance with those of other farmers, read John Nix's *Farm Management Pocketbook* which is up-dated every year and is jam-packed with figures and costings on every aspect of farming. It does not cost much and it is the paper farmer's bible.

Cow records

Dairy farms use all sorts of systems and aids in record-keeping and you can easily adapt these to your needs. The most basic is the card index: a card for each cow, on which your note every event in her life – date of birth, pedigree, dates of every service and calving, details of each calf, medical records, milk yields and so on. This system can consist of hand-written or typed cards filed in a box, or it can be computerised either on the farm or through the management services offered by the MMB or private bureaux and consultants. Computerised records can be analysed at the touch of a button to all sorts of parameters which, wisely chosen and used, can open your eyes to factors you had never considered: seasonal patterns, for example (do your cows conceive more readily in summer?), or the effects of feeding and pasture management, or trends traceable through mother, daughter and grand-daughter. Lactation curves can be revealing, too: if you draw a simple graph of milk yields for each cow (especially if you can do so daily) you will soon spot her bulling pattern, or the effects of ration changes or stressful situations.

Cow records should be designed so that they automatically produce some kind of visual future action chart, be it just a weekly diary or a graphic year planner. There are action wheels on the market which you could very easily adapt for smaller herds. You stick a tab with the cow's name on it on the day she is serviced and – magic – you will see at a glance when she needs to be watched for a return to service, or dried off before her next calving, or steamed up and brought in to calve.

Financial records

Book-keeping is a chore that some enjoy and most detest, but if you are at all serious about your enterprise you *must* keep on top of the books. Find a system (manual or computerised) which can provide quite a detailed analysis. It will help you see each month where too much money is going out, or which of several enterprises is a drain on the whole holding. Be strict about setting aside a few minutes every week to enter income and expenditure, and then *use* the records: analyse, consider, look ahead, make cashflow budgets, alter management practices when something is clearly going wrong.

Enterprise Costs

It is difficult to give an accurate idea of what your chosen enterprise is likely to cost in setting up and to run. Each situation is so individual, and prices can change considerably between the time of writing a book and the time you actually read it. I can only give you some idea of current prices and even then you will of course find differences due to the source of supply, your own bargaining skills, the advantages of bulk or co-operative purchasing, the availability of secondhand goods, and market fluctuations, especially in livestock and feedstuffs. The Appendix gives a table of prices and the addresses of several suppliers who cater for smallholders so that you can ask them for up-to-date catalogues and price-lists.

Grants and subsidies

Obtain a copy of the latest issue of the free MAFF booklet, *At the Farmer's Service*, to find out who might give you financial assistance. Talk to your MAFF divisional office or an agricultural consultant for advice, and have a word with the local county CoSIRA office. Contact your local council – they may want to encourage your enterprise (especially if it brings in tourists) – or the Countryside Commission if you have, say, a conservation angle.

The major grant schemes are AHGS (Agricultural and Horticultural Grant Scheme) and AHDS (Agricultural and Horticultural Development Scheme). The two particular schemes of interest to many smallholders (the Suckler Cow Premium Scheme and the Hill Livestock Compensatory Allowances) were discussed in Chapter 1.

There could also be grants for diversification and it may be that farm processing of produce will qualify for quite a reasonable grant, with assistance on feasibility studies and perhaps employment of marketing personnel as well. That augurs well for dairy dabblers.

Quotas

To produce milk, whomever you sell it to in whatever form, you need a quota. Quotas usually go with the land when you buy the holding.

Those who go over quota are penalised for producing too much milk in the quota year (which runs to the end of March) and if you look as if you are going over quota towards the end of the year you had better start feeding your milk to the pigs or making ice-cream. Quotas, frankly, are chaos: they were introduced very suddenly and unfairly, and no one ever seems to know what is going to happen or when. It is very much a case of paper farming and has nothing at all to do with good husbandry: some farmers do better out of buying, selling or leasing quotas as a commodity than out of milking cows.

Quotas are allocated to areas and if the whole area remains within quota no one needs to be penalised. The penalties are averaged out in several tiers: the whole country has a quota, and within the country, each region has a fraction of that quota, and so on. You do not in fact need to have a quota to register as a milk producer with the Government: the Ministry's milk registration certificate states that although you have a registration it does not mean you have a quota. Remember, the quota rules *at present* only refer to milk, cream, butter and cheese.

Quotas are registered with MMB, not the Ministry, and the MMB officer may be the best person to tell you about all the ins and outs of quotas and the little tricks of the trade practised by bigger, brasher farmers than yourself. There are many complications about trading in quotas: it is a whole enterprise in itself and seems alarmingly remote from the realities of cow-keeping. If your ambitions do not stretch further than keeping a couple of housecows, your priorities become much clearer and simpler: you aim to give your cows as good a life as possible, and you soon find that their saleable produce is almost incidental to the satisfaction which can be derived from looking after them well, sharing their company, watching their calves finding excitement in learning about the ways of the world and the other creatures with which they share it.

There is so much pleasure to be gained from keeping cows. They are such calm and generous animals, soothing to the soul (well, most of the time) and challenging to your ingenuity. They may be cumbersome, but they can inspire appreciative poetry and prose. Isak Dinesen caught the essence of cows in one of her *Seven Gothic Tales*:

'When bedtime came the boy had not been able to go to bed. Hot and bewildered, he had wandered about the farm buildings, seeking for something which might wash off this touch, and he had come down to the stables. It was a moonlight, misty night in early spring. Leaning against the wall, he had felt terribly lonely, and not only lonely, but betrayed, as if something were lying in wait for him. Then he had come to think of the cows inside, and of their imperturbability in the darkness. There was one big white cow, by the name of Rosa, which had been a favourite with the children. He had felt that she might give him comfort. Within her stall, his chest against the side of the reposing, gently chewing animal, a sweetly penetrating calm and balance had come upon him, and he had made up his mind to sleep with her all night. But hardly had he lain down in the straw when the stable door was opened gently, and a soft step approached. As he peeped over Rosa's back he saw the little girl come in, dim and light in the dim moonlight. She had been unhappy like him, he thought, and had felt that only a cud-chewing animal would have power to give her back her peace of heart.'

APPENDIX I

CONDITION SCORING

Stand behind the cow, making sure she is relaxed. Feel the amount of fatness in two places: her tailhead area and her loin. If the scores for each area differ by one point or more, adjust the tailhead score by half a point. Note that mature cattle can vary in weight by as much as 30kg in the same day. Use a calibrated tape-measure (weighband) to estimate weight from chest girth. (Rough guide: 100kg = 103.9cm; 200kg = 132.8cm; 300kg = 153.2cm; 400kg = 170.2cm; 500kg = 185.4cm; 600kg = 195.6cm.)

SCORE 1: POOR   Cavity present around tailhead. No fatty tissue felt between skin and pelvis. Ends of transverse processes of spine in loin area sharp to touch, upper surface easily felt. Deep depression in loin.

SCORE 2: MODERATE   Pin bones prominent. Some fatty tissue around tailhead. Pelvis easily felt. Ends of transverse processes feel slightly rounded. Visible depression in loin.

SCORE 3: GOOD   Fatty tissue easily felt over whole tailhead area. Skin smooth but pelvis can be felt. Ends of transverse processes felt with pressure but with thick layer of tissue on top. Slight loin depression visible.

SCORE 4: FAT   Folds of fatty tissue; patches of fat apparent under skin; no tailhead cavity at all; no visible loin depression between backbone and hip bones. Transverse processes cannot be felt even with firm pressure.

APPENDIX II

COW FACTS

HEART
45–60 beats per minute on average (take pulse at tail base).

LUNGS
Respiration rate normally 12–16 per minute.

TEMPERATURE
Average 101.3–103.1°F, 38–39°C.

MATURITY

Possible age of first bulling: 6–14 months.
Minimum age for first service: 15 months (2/3 mature weight).
Normal interval between heat periods: 18–24 days.
Duration of oestrus (heat period): 6–26 hours.
Time of ovulation: 10–15 hours after end of oestrus.
Average gestation period: 280 days (range 277–290).
Average lactation length: 305 days.
Average calving interval: 365 days.
Drying off: preferably at least 8 weeks before calving.

TEETH

Adult cattle: 32 teeth (8 incisors, 12 premolars, 12 molars).

Upper:	3	3	0	0	3	3
Lower:	3	3	4	4	3	3

AGE BY DENTITION

Like children, calves have milk teeth which are gradually replaced by permanent ones. You can obtain a rough idea of the age of a young animal by looking at its incisor (front) teeth. Incisors are named in pairs, starting at the middle pair: centrals, medials, laterals, corners.

AVERAGE AGE	CENTRALS	MEDIALS	LATERALS	CORNERS
At birth	Temporary	Temporary		
12–14 days			Temporary	
3–4 weeks				Temporary
1 year 10 months	Permanent			
2 years 6 months		Permanent		
3 years 2 months			Permanent	
3 years 9 months				Permanent

Premolars (front cheek teeth) are seen in young and adult cattle but the larger molars (back cheek teeth) are only seen in adults with permanent teeth.

APPENDIX III

FOOD TABLES

FOOD	DRY MATTER CONTENT [DM]	METABOLISABLE ENERGY [ME]	DIGESTIBLE CRUDE PROTEIN [DCP]
	g/kg	MJ/kg DM	g/kg DM
ROOTS			
Mangolds	100	12.4	80
Sugarbeet	200	13.7	35
Turnip	100	12.7	70
LEAVES			
Sugarbeet tops	160	9.9	88
Comfrey	120	8.5	130
Thousand-head kale	130	12.1	122
GRAZING, SILAGE, HAY			
Close-grazed pasture	200	12.1	225
Extensive grazing	200	10.0	124
Grass silage (high digestibility)	200	9.3	107
Grass hay (high digestibility)	850	9.0	58
BARLEY			
Barley straw, spring	860	7.3	9
Barley grain	860	12.9	82
Brewers' grains, dried	900	10.3	145
OTHER			
Fishmeal, white	900	11.1	631
Milk, whole (cow's)	128	20.2	250
Sugarbeet pulp, dried	900	12.7	61

APPENDIX IV

PLANTS TO AVOID

POISONOUS PLANTS

The following remain poisonous even after drying:

Bracken (green)
Bryony, white
Buckthorn
Cowbane and Water dropwort
Flax, Foxglove
Horsetails
Lily of the valley
Lupin

Pink family
Poppy family
Ragwort
Ranunculus family
Thornapple, Henbane
Nightshade
Yew

The following are poisonous when growing, and usually only if eaten in quantity:

Kale, rape and fodder beet in excess
Fresh sugarbeet tops (wilt them first)
Mangolds direct from the ground
Green potatoes, potato stems, potato leaves
Tomato stems and leaves
Oak leaves and acorns
Ash keys and fallen leaves
Spindle, box, mistletoe berries, ivy
Privet, rhododendron
Buckwheat, broomrape, charlock, white mustard, wild radish, horse-radish, hemlock, houndstongue, hypericum, meadow saffron, rushes (hard), sedum, sorrels, spurges and mercuries, tobacco, water figwort, bulbs, corms, rhizomes.

PLANTS WHICH AFFECT MILK

These plants might taint the milk, or cause problems with butter or cheese-making:

Buttercups
Butterwort
Chamomile
Chervil
Cow wheat
Fool's parsley
Garlic and onion
Hedge mustard

Ivy
Knotgrass and knotweed
Lesser watercress
Marsh marigold
Mint (prevents clotting)
Ox-eye daisy
Pennycress
Pepper saxifrage

Sage	Water parsnip
Sorrel (butter-making)	Wild radish
Spurge	Wood sorrel (affects churning)
Sugarbeet pulp (excess)	Wormwood
Tansy	Yarrow
Turnips	

APPENDIX V

DISEASES

NOTIFIABLE DISEASES

The following cattle diseases must be reported immediately to the police and/or the Ministry's Divisional Veterinary Officer:

Anthrax
Cattle plague
Enzootic bovine leucosis (EBL)
Foot-and-mouth disease
Pleuro-pneumonia
Tuberculosis
Warble fly
(Brucellosis or any abortion should be reported to the DVO.)

ZOONOSES

The following cattle diseases can also affect human beings:

Anthrax	Leptospirosis
Brucellosis	Ringworm
Foot-and-mouth disease	Salmonellosis
Infectious bovine keratoconjunctivitis	Tuberculosis

CONTROL SCHEMES

The Government monitors and controls several diseases in cattle:

Bovine tuberculosis is tested regularly.

Brucellosis is tested mainly through bulk-tank milk.

Enzootic bovine leucosis, infectious bovine rhinotracheitis and *leptospira hardjo* can be monitored within a voluntary health scheme run by ADAS.

Warble fly outbreaks are still the subject of an eradication scheme.

APPENDIX VI

COSTINGS

The costings listed below can only give a rough guide to prices at the time of writing. They obviously vary according to source of supply, quantity, materials, design, availability etc.

DAIRY AND PARLOUR

Batch pasteuriser (30 litres): £1,300
Butter churn (hand): £30
Butter churn (electric): £170–£185
Butter churn (end-over): £215
Cheese press: £13–£70
Cheese mould (steel): £18–£25
Cooler (in-churn): £50–£65
Cream separator (hand): £250
Cream separator (electric): £325–£1,800
Cream setting pan: £10–£20
Cream skimmer: £7–£10
Dairy thermometer: £7–£12
Ice-cream equipment (new):
    Automatic pasteuriser/cooler/storage vat: £6,000
    Automatic batch freezer: £5,000
Ice-cream/yogurt processing vat (100–450 litres): £2,000–£3,000
Milk churn (10–20 litres): £25–£70
Milking machines:
    Single-cow milker: £550–£600
    Double: £745–£900
Stainless steel bucket: £20–£25
Yogurt cabinet (batch): £500

FENCING

(Check whether prices include delivery – might be cheaper to collect material yourself 'ex wood', especially in quantity.)
Barbed-wire (200m 2-ply 4-point): £15
Post-rammer: £30
Stakes (each): chestnut 50p; treated softwood £1
Strainers: chestnut £2; treated softwood £3.60

Struts: chestnut 90p; treated softwood £1.60
Electric fencers: £50–£100
Polywire (200m): £5
Polytape (200m): £15

SUNDRIES

Anti-kick bar: £6
Balling gun: £6
Cattle halter: £11
Cattle water trough: £60
Cow tie-chain: £7–£10
Drench gun: £10–£50
Hayrack, portable: £10
Hoof knife: £5
Weighband: £5–£7

USEFUL ADDRESSES

BREED SOCIETIES

NATIONAL CATTLE BREEDERS' ASSOCIATION
   (for up-to-date list of breed society addresses)
   Cholesbury, Tring, Hertfordshire
RARE BREEDS SURVIVAL TRUST
   (for rare-breed society addresses)
   4th Street, National Agricultural Centre, Kenilworth, Warwickshire CV8 2LG
AYRSHIRE CATTLE SOCIETY
   PO Box 8, 1 Racecourse Road, Ayr KA7 2DE
BRITISH FRIESIAN CATTLE SOCIETY
   Scotsbridge House, Rickmansworth, Hertfordshire WD3 3BB
DEXTER CATTLE SOCIETY
   Whitehouse Farm, No Man's Heath, Tamworth, Staffordshire
ENGLISH GUERNSEY CATTLE SOCIETY
   The Bury Farm, Pednor Road, Chesham, Buckinghamshire HP5 2LA
GALLOWAY CATTLE SOCIETY
   Royal Bank of Scotland Buildings, 131 King Street, Castle Douglas DG7 1LZ
HIGHLAND CATTLE SOCIETY
   Blackchub, Keir, Thornhill, Dumfriesshire DG3 4DH
JERSEY CATTLE SOCIETY
   154 Castle Hill, Reading, Berkshire RG1 7RP

RED POLL & BRITISH DANE CATTLE SOCIETY
  6 Church Street, Woodbridge, Suffolk
SHORTHORN SOCIETY
  4th Street, National Agricultural Centre, Stoneleigh, Kenilworth, Warwickshire CV8 2LR
SOUTH DEVON HERD BOOK SOCIETY
  24 Courtenay Park, Newton Abbot, Devon TQ12 2HB
SUSSEX CATTLE SOCIETY
  Station Road, Robertsbridge, East Sussex TN32 5DG
WELSH BLACK CATTLE SOCIETY
  13 Bangor Street, Caernarfon, Gwynedd LL55 1AP

GENERAL

BRITISH TRUST FOR CONSERVATION VOLUNTEERS
  36 St Mary's Street, Wallingford, Oxfordshire OX10 0EU
CENTRE FOR ALTERNATIVE TECHNOLOGY
  Machynlleth, Powys
CoSIRA (COUNCIL FOR SMALL INDUSTRIES IN RURAL AREAS)
  141 Castle Street, Salisbury, Wiltshire SP1 3TP
DAIRY CREST FOODS
  Countrywide House, West Bar, Banbury, Oxfordshire
DEPARTMENT OF AGRICULTURE AND FISHERIES FOR SCOTLAND
  Chesser House, Gorgie Road, Edinburgh EH11 3AW
DEPARTMENT OF AGRICULTURE FOR NORTHERN IRELAND
  Dundonald House, Upper Newtownards Road, Belfast BT4 3SB
ENGLISH COUNTRY CHEESE COUNCIL
  National Dairy Centre (see below)
FARMING AND WILDLIFE ADVISORY GROUPS
  The Lodge, Sandy, Bedfordshire SG19 2DL
FOOD FROM BRITAIN
  Market Towers, New Covent Garden Market, 1 Nine Elms Lane, London SW8 5NQ
ICE CREAM ALLIANCE
  90/94 Gray's Inn Road, London WC1X 8AH
INTERMEDIATE TECHNOLOGY DEVELOPMENT GROUP
  9 King Street, London WC2E 8HN
INTERVENTION BOARD FOR AGRICULTURAL PRODUCE
  Fountain House, 2 Queens Walk, Reading, Berkshire RG1 7QW
MEAT & LIVESTOCK COMMISSION
  Queensway House, Bletchley, Milton Keynes MK2 2EF
MILK MARKETING BOARDS (FEDERATION OF)
  Thames Ditton KT7 0EL
MINISTRY OF AGRICULTURE, FISHERIES & FOOD
  Whitehall Place, London SW1A 2HH
MAFF PUBLICATIONS
  Lion House, Willowburn Estate, Alnwick, Northumberland NE66 2PF

NATIONAL DAIRY CENTRE
  5–7 John Princes Street, London W1M 0AP
WOAD (WELSH OFFICE AGRICULTURAL DEPARTMENT)
  Crown Offices, Cathays Park, Cardiff CF1 3NQ

MAGAZINES

THE ARK (Rare Breeds Survival Trust – monthly)
  4th Street, National Agricultural Centre, Kenilworth, Warwickshire CV8 2LG
DRAUGHT ANIMAL NEWS (Centre for Tropical Veterinary Medicine)
  University of Edinburgh, Easter Bush, Roslin, Midlothian
FARMERS WEEKLY (Reed Business Publishing – weekly)
  Carew House, Wallington, Surrey SM6 0DX
HOME FARM (Broad Leys Publishing Co. – bi-monthly)
  Buriton House, Station Road, Newport, Saffron Walden, Essex CB11 3PL
SMALLHOLDER (Charter Magazines Ltd – monthly)
  High Street, Stoke Ferry, King's Lynn, Norfolk PE33 9SF

SUPPLIERS

CLARENDON FOOD & DAIRY EQUIPMENT LTD
  12 Clarendon Place, Leamington Spa, Warwickshire CV32 5QW
R. J. FULLWOOD & BLAND LTD (milking machinery)
  Ellesmere, Shropshire SY12 9DF
GASCOIGNE MILKING EQUIPMENT LTD
  Edison Road, Houndmills, Basingstoke, Hampshire RG21 2YJ
LANDKEY-NEWLAND (distributors, Unilac milking machinery)
  Samosir, Newlands, Landkey, Barnstaple, Devon EX32 0ND
LINCOLNSHIRE SMALLHOLDERS SUPPLIES LTD
  Willow Farm, Thorpe Fendykes, Wainfleet, Skegness, Lincolnshire
  PE24 4QH
POLYBUILD (polypens etc.)
  Unit 5c, Tewkesbury Industrial Centre, Green Lane, Tewkesbury, Gloucester-
  shire GL20 8HD
SMALLHOLDING & FARM SUPPLY CO.
  Gerard Street, Heeley, Sheffield S8 9SJ
SMALLHOLDING SUPPLIES
  Little Burcott, Wells, Somerset BA5 1NQ

GLOSSARY

AFTERBIRTH   The placenta – membranes linking calf with cow while in the womb.

AFTERMATH   Regrowth for grazing after crop has been taken off the field.

BAG   Udder.

BAGGING UP   Rapid filling of udder just before calving.

BEESTINGS   Colostrum.

BLOAT or BLOW   Condition in which animal cannot expel fermentation gases from rumen, which becomes distended.

BOBBY   Very young calf sold for meat.

BULL   Entire male aged 180 days or more.

BULLDOG   Deformed calf (short legs, swollen abdomen, foreshortened jaws) sometimes born to Dexters – hereditary condition.

BULLING   In oestrus and ready for mating.

BULLOCK   Castrated bull.

CALF   Young animal up to 180 days old.

CALVING INTERVAL   Number of days between consecutive calvings for a particular cow. 'Calving index' is the whole herd's average. Ideal is 365 days in either case.

CLAW   (a) One of the pair of hooves on each foot.
         (b) In milking machinery, a unit connecting a set of teat-cup tubes to their pulse and milk tubes.

CLEANSE   To expel afterbirth.

CLUSTER   In milking machinery, a unit consisting of the claw and the four teat-cups and their tubes.

COLOSTRUM   First milk produced by newly calved cow, usually for four days; thick yellow substance rich in antibodies and other proteins, vitamins and minerals.

CONCENTRATES   Foods rich in proteins and/or carbohydrates; high dry-matter content; easily digested.

CROSSBRED   The offspring of two different breeds.

DAIRY HERD   Officially defined as one or more cows milked, managed and recorded as a single unit.

DISBUDDING   Removal of horn buds in young calf to prevent development of horns.

DOWN-CALVER   Cow nearing end of pregnancy.

DRENCH   Fluid given orally, usually for medicinal purposes, by trickling the liquid carefully down the animal's throat.

DRY   Not producing milk.

DUAL-PURPOSE   Bred to give both meat and milk.

EMBRYO and FOETUS   The conceived organism is an embryo up to day 42 of life, and a foetus thereafter until it is born.

EMPTY   Not in calf.

FINCHING   Typical colouring in certain breeds (eg Longhorn, Gloucester), also known as 'lineback': a white dorsal stripe running along the back, under the tail and along the underside.

FINISH   Stage at which beef cattle are ready for slaughter.

FORAGE   Plant material (except in concentrated feeds) fed to cattle.

FOREMILK   The first milk drawn from each teat.

FREEMARTIN   Sterile heifer, twin to a bull calf.

GADDING   Restlessness caused by irritation from flies.

GRADING SYSTEM   Method of evaluating finished cattle for any subsidy support payments. (Minimum 380kg steers, 330kg heifers.)

GRADING UP   Building up a pedigree herd from non-pedigree cows by repeated use of pedigree bulls over several generations.

GRASSLAND   Type of plant community dominated by herbaceous species such as grass and clover.

HEAT   See OESTRUS.

HEIFER   Young cow aged 180 days or more who has not yet had a calf, or (colloquially) who has not yet reached her second lactation.

HUSK or HOOSE   Disease caused by parasitic lungworms.

IN-CALF   Pregnant.

LACTATION   Period over which a cow produces milk.

OESTRUS   Physiological state in which a female is ready for mating.

OESTRUS CYCLE   Number of days from start of one oestrus to start of next. (First day of oestrus counts as Day 0.)

OX   Castrated bull – usually applied to a draught animal.

pH   Measure of acidity or alkalinity of a solution (potential of hydrogen). pH of pure water = 7; acid <7; alkali >7.

POLLED   Born without the ability to develop horns.

ROUGHAGE   Bulk food high in fibre.

SCOURS or SKITS   Diarrhoea.

SERVICE   Natural mating or artificial insemination during oestrus.

SILAGE   Green crops (especially grass) preserved in moist, acid state with air excluded.

STAGGERS   Condition arising from lack of bloodstream magnesium.

STANDING HEAT/OESTRUS   Period during bulling when cow will stand voluntarily to be mounted.

STEAMING UP   Increased feeding (concentrates) of a down-calver.

STEER   Young castrated bull intended for beef.

STIRK   Maiden heifer, i.e. one who has not been served.

STOCKING RATE   Number of cattle per unit area of grazing etc.

STOCKING, SET   Fixed number of cattle having unrestricted access to specific area for most of the grazing season.

STORE CATTLE   Beef animals maintained on economic surplus food and not expected to make gains.

STRIP   To milk out the last drops from the teats.

STRIP GRAZING   Grazing controlled by electric fence to give access to fresh strip of grazing daily (preferably with back-up fence to prevent grazing of regrowth).

SUCCULENT   Food with high moisture content and palatability.

TRIPLE-PURPOSE   Bred to give meat, milk and muscle-power.

ZERO GRAZING   Feeding system in which forage is cut and carted to the cow.

BIBLIOGRAPHY

BARRON, Norman: *Dairy Farmer's Veterinary Book* 9th edition, 1976, Farming Press Ltd.

BLACK, Maggie: *Home-made Butter, Cheese and Yoghurt*, 1977, EP Publishing Ltd.

BLAKE, P. W. (ed): *Livestock Production*, 1975, William Heinemann Ltd.

CASTLE, Malcolm E., and WATKINS, Paul: *Modern Milk Production*, 1979, Faber & Faber.

COBBETT, William: *Cottage Economy*, 1823, reprinted 1974, Landsman's Bookshop.

COOPER, Michael: *Discovering Farmhouse Cheese*, 1978, Shire Publications.

DALTON, Clive: *An Introduction to Practical Animal Breeding*, 1985, Collins.

DE BAIRACLI LEVY, Juliette: *Herbal Handbook for Farm and Stable*, revised 1973, Faber & Faber.

DINESEN, Isak: *Seven Gothic Tales*, 1952, Penguin Modern Classics.

DUBACH, Josef: *Traditional Cheesemaking*, translated by Bill Hogan, 1987, Intermediate Technology Publications.

FRASER, Andrew F.: *Farm Animal Behaviour*, 1980, Bailliere Tindall.

HALLEY, R. J. (ed): *The Agricultural Notebook*, 17th edition, 1982, Butterworth Scientific.

HART, Edward: *Showing Livestock*, 1979, David & Charles.

HINKS, John: *Breeding Dairy Cattle*, 1983, Farming Press Ltd.

KILGOUR, Ronald, and DALTON, Clive: *Livestock Behaviour*, 1984, Granada Publishing Ltd.

NIX, John: *Farm Management Pocketbook*, Wye College, Ashford.

ORSKOV, Bob: *The Feeding of Ruminants*, 1987, Chalcombe Publications.

PORTER, Valerie: *Practical Rare Breeds*, 1987, Pelham Books Ltd.

ROTHWELL, J.: *Ice Cream Making*, Ice Cream Alliance.

RUSSELL, Kenneth: *The Principles of Dairy Farming*, 10th edition, 1985, Farming Press Ltd.

SAINSBURY, David: *Farm Animal Welfare*, 1986, William Collins Sons & Co. Ltd.

SCOTT, W. N. (ed): *The Care and Management of Farm Animals*, 1978, Bailliere Tindall.

SPAULDING, C. E.: *A Veterinary Guide for Animal Owners*, 1976, Rodale Press Inc.

SPRECKLEY, Val: *Keeping a Cow*, 1979, David & Charles.

STOUT, Adam: *The Old Gloucester*, 1980, Alan Sutton Publishing.

STREET, Len, and SINGER, Andrew: *The Backyard Dairy Book*, 1975, Prism Press.

TAMINE, A. Y. and ROBINSON, R. K.: *Yoghurt – Science and Technology*, Pergamon Press.

THEAR, Katie: *The Home Dairying Book,* 1978, Broad Leys Publishing Co.

TOUSSAINT RAVEN, E.: *Cattle Footcare and Claw Trimming*, 1985, Farming Press.

VAN LOON, Dirk: *The Family Cow*, 1976, Garden Way Publishing.

WILKINSON, J. M.: *Milk and Meat from Grass,* 1984, Granada in association with BSP Professional.

PUBLICATIONS FROM AGRICULTURAL AND DAIRY ORGANISATIONS

BRITISH TRUST FOR CONSERVATION VOLUNTEERS:
> *Hedging*
> *Dry Stone Walling*

RURAL RESETTLEMENT GROUP:
> *Rural Resettlement Handbook*, 3rd ed, 1984, Prism Alpha.

MAFF:
> *Calf Rearing*
> *Dairy Herd Fertility*
> *Energy Allowances and Feeding Systems for Ruminants*
> *Management of the Dairy Cow*
> *Management of the Spring Calving Dairy Herd*
> *Nutrient Allowances and Composition of Feedingstuffs for Ruminants*
> *At the Farmer's Service*
> *Farmhouse Butter Making*
> *Farmhouse Production of Clotted Cream*
> *Farmhouse Production of Cream*
> *Farmhouse Production of Yogurt*

MMB:
> *Dairy Facts and Figures*
> *On-Farm Cheese Makers of England and Wales*
> *Report of the Breeding and Production Organisation*

NATIONAL DAIRY COUNCIL:
> *Facts About Cream*
> *Facts About Cheese*
> *Facts About Yogurt*
> *A Handbook of Dairy Foods*
> *Whey*

INDEX

Cows for the Smallholder